THE FRIENDLY YEAR

Plough shallow, and you'll get a worthless crop. Plough deep, and you'll get a good harvest, most years. What you put in you get out. The patient soil never really lets you down. God's the same —only neither God nor the soil will stand being hurried. Not that it hurts *them*, of course, but hurrying makes a fool of *you*.'

A Philosopher of the Soil, page 31

THE FRIENDLY YEAR

BY

H. L. GEE

THE EPWORTH PRESS
(EDGAR C. BARTON)
25-35 CITY ROAD, LONDON, E.C.1

Made in Great Britain

To

MAURICE A. R. HORSPOOL,

FRIEND OF MANY FRIENDLY YEARS

Many of the adventures related in the following pages appeared as 'Friendly Man' articles in *The Methodist Recorder*. They are incorporated in this book by kind permission of the Editor.

CONTENTS

10 *Contents*

FOREWORD

If I chose, and if Judith agreed, I believe I could write a book called *The Unfriendly Year*. At any rate, one would expect such an undertaking to be a very simple matter, for I might easily set down some of the unhappy incidents belonging to any twelve months of my life. I can say with truth that people who have borrowed from me have failed to pay back. People I have gone out of my way to help have forgotten to say, 'Thank you'. People I have trusted have let me down. Most certainly it would be no hard task to gather into book-form a series of reminiscences such as these, *if only I could recall them*.

That is the difficulty. Happily, I have forgotten most of these unhappy things, and even were I to bring them to mind again, Judith would no doubt prohibit their publication by saying sweetly, 'You may please yourself, dear', in such a tone that I could not possibly go on.

Looking back over a year of my life, then, I seem to have no alternative but to pass over the shadows as if they had never been (though God's face is often brightest when the light is dim), and to remember only the sunny hours.

What have these twelve months done for me?

They have led me into so many adventures, introduced me to so many kindly folk, blessed me with so much good, enriched me with such wealth, that I cannot recall them without being glad and thankful. It has been a friendly year indeed. Much there has been to deplore, but there has been so much to thank God for in the past that I dare to look forward with confidence to the future.

H. L. GEE.

MRS. WHISPERING WILLIAMS

I AM NOT LIKELY to forget that winter evening, though I never recall it without a twinge of conscience.

Some one came knocking at our door about seven, and I confess it was not a welcome sound, for there was nothing I wanted that January evening so much as to be left alone with Judith. She and I were sitting by the fire, she bending over one of my socks, the lamplight blessing her, the firelight playing upon her face, while I pretended to read between nods which were becoming alarmingly frequent. Suddenly Judith exclaimed: 'Some one's at the door.'

'Tell them we're out,' I murmured, an observation of which I was instantly ashamed.

My wife, a better Christian than I ever hope to be, suggested I should answer the door, which I did, opening it to find the lady who lives close by. We call her Mrs. Whispering Williams because she is a nervous little body, with a tiny, husky voice, steel-rimmed spectacles, and a rather odd way of telling you commonplace news as if it is some tremendous secret.

I should have opened the door more readily to almost any one else. Mrs. Williams has a disturbingly fussy manner, not to mention an embarrassing way of *not* being able to go when you feel it is time for her to depart; and I may as well add that the minute I saw her I knew my evening was ruined.

She came in, of course. I could not turn her from the door, so I asked her to step in out of the cold and wet. She was pleased to come, apologizing for her damp umbrella, and offering to carry it into the scullery. She didn't want to be any trouble, she said; and if we had friends she wouldn't come in on any account. Were we *quite* sure it would be all right if she stayed just a few minutes, and wasn't it a wretched evening, and would we *please* go on doing what we had been doing?

It took her ages to settle down, she was so anxious not to disturb us. She whispered all the time, pulling her chair up to Judith's in order to show her a number of photographs of people of whom my wife had never heard. As for me, I filled my pipe and leaned back in my chair as one determined to master the contents of a great book, Judith having hinted that I *must* finish my reading before going to bed. But what with trying *not* to hear Mrs. Williams's everlasting whispers, and very earnestly endeavouring, in spite of myself, to catch what she said, I am afraid I gathered a rather meagre literary harvest.

There seemed no end to the photographs of people we had not seen, but Judith and I (for

I was roped in in due course) were commendably polite, I think; and we really did try to conjure up a little enthusiasm, even though we kept one eye on the clock. Eventually Judith essayed a gentle hint, inquiring graciously if Mrs. Williams would care to take coffee with us. Our guest fussed a little before assuring us that she would be glad to stay *to please us*.

So she stayed, and we had coffee and biscuits by the fire; and I happened to be putting down my spoon when I caught sight of her face at the very moment Judith looked up. To our astonishment we saw the tears streaming down her thin cheeks, and before we quite knew what was happening, little Mrs. Whispering Williams was saying: 'Do forgive me, *please*. It's because of Arthur, you know. You couldn't be expected to remember, but this happens to be the tenth anniversary of the night they brought him home, dead. It was *such* a shock.'

She was staring into the fire. 'I know you'll understand,' she whispered. 'Somehow this anniversary of Arthur's death seems worse than any of the others. I felt a little while ago that I just couldn't stay in the house *alone*. I've several good neighbours, but yours is the only house where I feel I dare come uninvited. You've both been so sweet to me; so kind. You've helped me over a bad time, and you'll never know what it has meant to me. . . .'

Half an hour later she took my arm as we
groped our way through the darkness to her
house. She shivered at the door. 'Arthur was
very wonderful,' she whispered, 'and he had
odd ways of doing good in secret. I've tried to
honour his memory all these years, and I think
I may say I've kept up all the little ser····
which were so dear to his heart. I hope he's
pleased with me.'

I raised my hat as I turned to go, though the
night was too dark for her to see me do it; and,
oddly enough, I wanted to laugh. I wanted
to laugh, not at Mrs. Whispering Williams, but
at the quaint thought she had put into my
head, for never till that moment had it ever
occurred to me that a woman who wore steel-
rimmed spectacles might be a saint!

For that matter, it had never occurred to me
that in this commonplace world one might by
chance live almost next door to a saint, though
I realized, as I walked home, that *somebody* must
have lived next door to St. Paul long before he
found a place in a stained glass window.

I say I wanted to laugh, but there was
something like a catch in my throat, for I was
conscious of how little I had done to make
Mrs. Williams welcome, and of how wonderfully she had braved the bleak years since
Arthur died. We had often laughed at her,
Judith and I; but suddenly we came to realize

that this little, timid woman with the steel-rimmed spectacles was a heroine, and something of a saint; and that instead of being bitter because of the rude treatment Fate had meted out to her, she had tried earnestly and constantly to keep on doing the lovely things Arthur had delighted to do.

BY THE FIRE

MUCH MAY BE SAID in praise of winter.

In spite of the fact that it is often dismal and depressing, it sometimes gives us magic days under a steel-blue sky, days when the wind has a tang, and when a vast silence seems to rest upon a world filled with gaunt splendour.

To me, winter is one of the most friendly of all seasons. It robs us of sunshine, but it gives us long nights when no one dreams of turning out, every evening an excuse for gathering round the fire after shutting out the darkness and keeping in the light and love. In summer we are in danger of dispersing, each going his own way, all finding or making their own pleasures and amusements; but in winter we are more often drawn together under one roof and round one fire, a kind of domestic altar where we may worship God without knowing what we are about. Keeping our tempers near the hearth is an acceptable sacrifice, surely; humour is incense, fellowship with one another is almost communion with Him; and our quiet talk in the firelight, our intimate understandings, pleasant reminiscences, and half-told dreams, even our gossip and laughter, may serve to instil into our souls the spirit which makes it easy for us to feel after God, and find Him.

I recall, however, a winter evening when I did not stay by my own fire, Judith having issued an ultimatum to the effect that certain ladies would be taking possession of the lounge for a few hours. As modesty happens to be one of my many virtues, I accordingly bethought me of a way I frequently adopt of enjoying a profitable evening beyond my own front door.

I did not go to the theatre. I did not patronize a cinema. I did not draw up plans for a big business campaign, and I most certainly did not wear a paper hat at a party. In point of fact, I smoked some of Fred's tobacco as I sat by Fred's fireside, and talked with Fred's wife—and occasionally with Fred.

It was comforting to feel that I was there without having first received a printed card with R.S.V.P. in the bottom left-hand corner. It was pleasant to find no elaborate display of silver and glass and china on the table, for the simple reason that supper was no more than coffee, biscuits, and cheese, your cup on the floor, your plate in your hand, and your toes toasting near the hearth. No formality. No fuss. No excitement. No expense, to speak of—a point worth noting in these days.

What happened, you perceive, was that the idea of strolling round to Fred's had popped into my head. Had he been out, I should have strolled back home. As he happened to be in, I opened the front door, called out, 'It's only me' (trusting that St. Peter pardons grammatical errors), and hung my hat in the hall.

'Don't come in,' Fred shouted over his shoulder.

'Thanks for the welcome,' I murmured.

'I suppose you can't stay long?' my host inquired anxiously.

I assured him that I could stay three or four hours, whereupon he remarked that he and his wife had been having a pleasant time till my arrival. Thus encouraged, I beamed upon him, helped myself (as I said) to his tobacco, and added insult to injury by 'borrowing' a match. When Fred gave me a hint that it was about time to go, I blandly informed him that I couldn't possibly go into the cold without a cup of coffee.

In this pleasant way, therefore, I settled down in the armchair facing Fred, with Annie between us. She was knitting socks for that boy of theirs who is so dear to their hearts, and though her knitting was fast and furious her face was placid as ever, her words kindly.

Well, I think that is all I have to say. You wouldn't be very interested in our conversation, though it interested *us*. We talked about the international situation. I propounded certain theories, and Fred let his pipe go out while propounding others. I am not sure which of us was farthest from the truth. We discussed church membership; and we became quite warm over the matter of a new heating apparatus in the chapel we both attend. Fred told me again how the most serious illness he had ever had had wrought a miracle in his soul; and Annie put down her knitting to say that she had always been afraid of bad times, but that now they were here she was so busy cheering her old ladies, of whom, like Judith, she has quite a collection, that she had never had time to fret. I told them both about an experience which changed my life—a five minutes' conversation with a man of God whose face was a sermon and whose smile made one long to be good. . . .

I cannot remember anything else worth mentioning. It was raining a little when I left them, and Fred said rather sulkily that I might borrow the umbrella he'd borrowed from some one, though he couldn't remember who.

Do you wonder what all this is about? Do

you think it dull and uninteresting? Have you
been waiting for a climax? Surely you see that
in these harassing days a chat by the fire with
true friends, the fellowship of the hearth, the
privilege of sharing the sanctuary of a home,
these are among life's greatest joys. Will you
forgive me for saying I worshipped there by
Fred's hearth, and came away with my soul
buttressed against every storm? Do you see
now why winter seems such a friendly season;
and do you wonder that when Judith asked
me where I had been, I was momentarily
tempted to say I had been sitting in the outer
courts of the Temple?

THE TRIVIAL ROUND

I OUGHT PERHAPS to explain that when I called
on Fred I knocked at his front door before opening it. I opened his *front* door because Judith
has at last succeeded in inculcating rudimentary
good manners in me; but now and then I slip
back into utterly deplorable barbarity, having
a kind of inherent weakness for *back doors*.

Give me half a chance, and I forsake the
dignified front door for the more humble and
friendly back door of anybody's house. I once
knocked at the back door of a large house in

Yorkshire, and was rewarded for my trespass upon conventionality by hearing a woman call out from an upper window, 'No onions nor apples to-day, thanks!' But the *dénouement* led to a very happy understanding, and I never pass that house now without calling for a chat.

On the February day which comes to mind I began with the words: 'Good morning! You seem happy!'

'Goodness, what a start you *did* give me,' said a voice.

'Madam,' I replied politely (trying hard to live up to the high standard Judith ever keeps before me), 'I rang the front door bell, and then knocked, even as Peter did when the damsel Rhoda opened not unto him. So I *had* to come to the back door.'

'I have to keep the scullery door closed,' she explained. 'The draught blows the oven gas out, and I'm baking.'

'And singing,' said I.

She admitted the charge. '*Do* come in,' she begged, 'and excuse my apron. You really *did* take me unawares, you know. I'll just finish beating this Yorkshire pudding, and then we'll go into the lounge.'

'Why not talk *here*?'

'What—in the scullery?'

'Why not? I can lean against the table, if you'll let me, and you can talk while seeing to the baking and the cooking. We may as well stay, don't you think?'

'Of course. But it isn't done.'

'My dear lady, less than five minutes ago you were in heaven, isn't that so? You were singing in your scullery. It seems to me that if this part of the house is good enough for *you* it ought to be good enough for *me*. Couldn't we *both* be in heaven a few minutes, don't you think?'

She had gone back to the little table near the sink. Very attractive she looked in her coloured apron, the sunshine falling upon her face—a little flushed, perhaps, with cooking. Her gas-stove shone. The pan-lids on the shelf behind her glinted like silver. The blue and white bowl in which the thick saffron-coloured batter curled about the spoon was a picture in itself— smile if you will.

'Yes,' she said slowly, 'I think I *was* in heaven. Do you know, I rather think I'm happier in this sunny scullery than anywhere else, except when John and I are together somewhere.'

She said it so simply and naturally that I knew she was taking me into her confidence.

'You know,' she went on happily, smiling as she spoke, 'I think I'm made to be happy in *ordinary* places. John and I went on tour in Scotland one July—I must tell you all about it some time. We'd a wonderful holiday among the Trossachs, and it was all thrilling. But you don't know how thrilled I was to be home again—to see the dear little house once more. I felt it was lonely without me, somehow; and John looked nervous when I patted the front door and told it I was home again. . . .

'And of all the rooms in the house, well, I dare say I really *am* happiest here in the scullery. I *love* cooking. I *enjoy* washing up!'

'And I enjoy drying pots,' said I. 'You've a stack of them there, so if the baking's done, may I lend a hand?'

She paused. Then, laughing, she said, 'Very well! I'll just put these tarts on the wire tray, and *then* we'll wash up together; and I'll tell John I've had a gentleman to dry the pots. He'll be yellow with jealousy, bless him. It *is* fun, really, isn't it, if you look at it in this way? I mean, after all, going to the pictures, or taking a holiday, or paying a call . . . they're *occasional* pleasures, aren't they? But if a woman loves housework, if she adores her home, even if it's small like mine, and if she likes to make a palace of her scullery where (whether she will or not) so much of her time *must* be spent, why, as the old hymn says very truly:

> The trivial round, the common task,
> Will furnish all we ought to ask,
> Room to deny ourselves, a road
> To bring us daily nearer God.

Don't you agree?'

I said I did, and I suggested we should sing the verse while she washed and I dried.

I venture to think, by the way, that any road may bring us nearer to God, even a lonely road— but a friendly road is best of all, usually bringing us more speedily into the glory of His presence.

At any rate, I have often found it so, and my mind goes back to a bright February afternoon, and to the droll incident which took place so quickly that it was over almost before I knew it had begun.

'Please, I'se lost,' she said.

Being market day, the town was busy. Pausing on the crowded pavement, I looked down at the bairn—she could not have been more than five—who had singled me out. She wore a furry brown coat and hood, with brown shoes to match. An exceptionally pretty child, she had large eyes, and a rather quaint and roguish look. 'Lost?' I repeated.

She nodded gravely. There were no tears. There was no quivering of the lip. She stated quite simply and plainly that she was lost, just as she might have said that she liked buns with pink icing.

'Well,' I murmured, somewhat taken aback by her calm declaration, and rather embarrassed by the situation, for I had no time to spare, 'how did you get lost?'

She did not answer my question. Instead, she

slipped her small hand into mine. 'Tate me home, *please*,' she whispered.

'But your mother?' said I. 'She may be looking for you.'

'No. She doesn't know I've tum.'

'Do you mean you've come out without telling her?'

She nodded. 'She thinks I've just gone to see Elsa,' this odd child informed me, her self-possession and air of quiet assurance never forsaking her. 'But I haven't.'

'Where do you live?'

She told me—and I whistled. It was a good mile or more. 'How did you come to town?' I demanded.

'I just tummed. I walked on my two feet. I'se tired.'

'You *walked*?' I stared. 'Alone? But why?'

'I didn't want Mummie to know. I just wanted to have a surprise for her.'

'But wouldn't it have been better to come with your father?'

She sighed, evidently tired of my questions, and the least bit disappointed that I did not help her as she wished. Shaking her head she said: '*He's* lost, too.'

She bewildered me. 'Lost?' I repeated.

'At sea.'

It was these words which impressed me. They were so simple. She was innocent of their true and full import, I gathered, repeating what she had heard without understanding. I understood, however, and I began to see something of what was in her mind. 'Tell me why you came,' I said, picking her up, and carrying her along the pavement.

'To spend a penny Granny gave me,' was the reply. 'But the lady in the shop said it wasn't enough.' The big eyes suddenly filled with tears, the lip quivered. I felt two small arms tighten about my neck. 'Mummie said to a lady that nobody ever brings flowers now Daddy's lost at sea. So I just thought I would tum and buy a bunch for a penny. . . .'

'And you lost your way?'

'Yes.'

'And you hadn't enough money?'

She was sobbing on my shoulder. 'The fairies told me to tum,' she said, as best she could, 'but they didn't take care of my feet.'

So I comforted her as best I could; and presently we went into a flower shop where I bought a bowl of hyacinths, the little maid cheering up bravely. Wiping her eyes, she smiled at me with that quaint little smile of hers. Then we boarded a tram, and before long we were near her home. In she went, all eagerness. 'Mummie,' she called, 'I've bought you some flowers, and there's a man outside!'

I stayed long enough to explain what had

happened; and when I found myself talking to a woman with a handsome, pale face, and eyes very like those of the little maid I had carried, I ventured to add that God is good, and that when a husband is lost at sea there is often a little child to lead us along the road to heaven.

She thanked me, and the little maid whispered that the fairies had looked after *my* feet instead of hers.

As I came away I could do no other than thank God that there is yet so much that is sweet and good in the world.

If the friendly year I delight to recall has taught me anything, it has taught me that nothing on earth can finally destroy beauty, either in field and wood, or in the heart and soul of men and women. The loveliness which is the visible joy God feels may be eclipsed, but it shines again and again. After the storm— and what storms there are in the depth of winter—comes the promise of spring.

BEHOLD, I MAKE ALL THINGS NEW

I REMEMBER ONE DAY.

I was alone. Up hill and down I went, over the bridge, and then, turning off from the high road, along a green lane, where the snow still lay in the blue shadows, and ice sparkled in the wheel-tracks, silence brooding over all.

I will own that the first few weeks of the year had tried my patience. I was tired of the cold. I was perhaps a little depressed, for the sadness and anxiety of the times seemed to be seeping into my soul, much as the snow had come through the roof of my house, staining a bedroom ceiling.

It was good to be out of town, however; good to have the hills for company, and the great trees, the open spaces, the loneliness, and the silence. No one asked if I had listened-in to the one o'clock news. No one said things were looking serious. No one had a word to say, for no one was there—and that, for once in a while, was a good thing.

It would be strange if a man were not a little disturbed in these momentous days. Always to be gay is not necessarily to vindicate faith, but rather to tell the world you are shallow at heart. At any rate, so it seems to me; and whether it be so or not, I was burdened as I tramped through the sunshine with anxieties and misgivings.

Thus it was that quite unexpectedly I came upon a sight to stir the very heart of me.

I swung round a corner—for I was tramping on unobservantly, my mind a prey to many thoughts—when I stood still. There, among the trees, on the sunny and the sheltered side of a little bank, was a carpet of snowdrops.

They were the first I had seen.

I know not what you will think, and to speak the truth, I care very little, *but there in the lane I took off my hat.*

With frail green stems, modest bell-like flowers, tiny spears, the snowdrops were a peace-army, a silent surpliced choir, a host of gallant saints, an advance guard of all the flowers the year was yet to bring. To me, as I stood before them, they were a text in white and green. *Be of good courage*, they said. They were a covenant—God's living handwriting in a lonely place: *Behold, I make all things new!*

I thought: The world is mad. But the snowdrops are here again! Nothing can prevent their return. Out of the cold dark earth they have struggled to beauty and purity, to life and sweetness.

Had they no message?

I heard as it had been the sound of angels' wings, and I thought the trees bowed, as if the wind of God's passing smote them; and behold, a lark sprang up from the field beyond, and suddenly I felt a rush of new strength, the birth of a new joy, and the resurrection of a new faith.

Dark indeed may be the days of our winter,

but every winter turns to spring. God's snow-drops never fail; and God's saints upon the battle-field of life never lose their hold upon Him.

I did not gather any snowdrops. I dare not touch them. They taught me that hatred cannot quench love, that death cannot hold life everlasting prisoner.

Home I went with the snowdrops in my heart, praying all the way that springtime might ever lead me nearer to God, who in His good time brings beauty out of ugliness, good-ness out of what seems ill, and joy out of sorrow.

A PHILOSOPHER OF THE SOIL

THIS FEBRUARY DAY reminds me of the March day when Judith felt a sudden urge to begin spring-cleaning, and when, in consequence, I became imbued with a desire to worship nature out of doors; which I did.

Walking briskly in the sunshine I came to a five-barred gate, white in a hedge already showing promise of burning with green flame. Having little breath to spare for the uphill climb ahead, I rested my arms on the gate, and stood watching two horses coming up the field, fol-lowed by the ploughman.

Slowly they drew near, the horses straining steadily, their heads down, their massive bodies lunging forward. Now and then the ploughman gave the handles of the plough a dextrous turn with his strong, brown hands; but in the main, horses, plough, and ploughman were a unit, all making up a single implement for digging deep into the good earth.

As he reached the end of the furrow I nodded. He nodded back in a friendly way, and when the horses were facing downhill again, ready to begin another furrow, he pushed back his old hat, and mopped his forehead as he took a few strides towards me. 'Warm work coming up,' said he.

'Yes,' I agreed. 'You've a stiff soil there.'

'Aye, it's clay, and we're going deep.'

'You find it tiring? I expect you're ready for bed as soon as the day's done?'

'I am that. *But it's grand being tired.*'

'Of course. Still, one may be *too* tired, you know.'

'Aye, a man *can* if he *will*. But he's no business to be.'

'Oh, I don't know. Sometimes we *have* to keep on and on if we mean to get a piece of work done in time.'

'Well, in that case you should have begun sooner.'

'Yes, but you can't *always* do that, you know.'

'No, well, perhaps not. But that's usually because somebody's bungled. At any rate, in farming it's mostly different. A man's never supposed to slack off, but there's no need for him to do *more* than a fair day's work. As a rule it doesn't pay to work overtime; and it *never* pays to hurry.'

I laughed. 'Well,' I said, 'that may be right enough on a farm, but the world as a whole has other views. Most of us spend our lives trying to catch ourselves up.'

'Aye, no doubt. But if you wouldn't run so sharp you'd do it quicker. We weren't meant to spend our lives being in a hurry. It makes us do our work badly, and that's an affront to the Almighty, who always does *His* job well, and takes His time about it. Haste makes folk irritable and anxious and fearful. It robs 'em of peace of mind and quietness of spirit, and it won't give 'em *chance* to listen to what God's got to say. Besides, *they get less done.*'

I did not smile. I looked over the gate at the honest weathered face, the face of a man turned sixty, a man with a rugged exterior but the spirit of a quiet gentleman, an artist in living. And I looked beyond him to the patient horses, standing there till he should call; and farther still to the spacious field with its straight furrows ready for a harvest in God's good time; and somehow the sweet reasonableness of

Cy

all he had said sank into my soul, and I felt that indeed men were fools to be city-driven all their days, travelling such a little way in spite of all the noise and fuss.

He was speaking again: 'Mind you, it's only *my* way of looking at it,' he was saying. 'I was born here in the country, and I've had my feet in the soil ever since. I'm content. The Almighty's stood by me till now, and I'm reminded of Him at every step, for the soil's as near like Him as can be. Plough shallow, and you'll get a worthless crop. Plough deep, and you'll get a good harvest, most years. What you put in you get out. The patient soil never really lets you down. God's the same—only neither God nor the soil will stand being hurried. Not that it hurts *them*, of course, but hurrying makes a fool of *you*.'

Then he replaced his battered hat, and with a friendly nod, turned back, took up the handles, called softly to the horses, and went striding across the faithful, patient soil, his eyes on some distant landmark to help him plough a straight furrow.

There was something so splendid and sturdy about this son of the soil with a simple and immensely convincing philosophy, that he has since taken a sure place in my thoughts beside a young local preacher for whom I have a great regard. It would seem that hard work had sweetened rather than soured my ploughman friend, and I think the sheer struggle of life has strengthened rather than weakened Harry.

. At any rate, hard times have not lessened his appetite, and the way he praises Judith's baking by 'tucking in' whenever he comes to supper is as alarming as it is gratifying.

THE LOCAL PREACHER

I CAME ACROSS HIM in the spring of the year, and I have since been profoundly glad that I made his acquaintance. To some of you who have been dispirited lately, and have been in peril of becoming self-pitying souls, I would say, take Harry.

Take him anywhere you like—though the chances are he will be taking *you* out of the shadow of these days into the radiant presence of the Master he rejoices to serve, and the Saviour he is never afraid to preach.

He will also take you into his study, if he has half a chance. A pleasant, dignified, scholarly word, *study*, conjuring up visions of a spacious, well-carpeted apartment with thousands of handsomely bound books on oak shelves. Harry's study is the small bedroom over the hall, and you haven't to open the door too wide

as you go in, or you'll knock a doll's house over.
There is cheap linoleum on the floor, and a
mat. There is a tiny electric radiator—but
who needs artificial heat when the heart's afire
with God? There's a chair and table, and a
shelf of books, quite a dozen books, probably
nearly twenty, not counting, of course, *John
Wesley's Journal*, in eight handsome black
volumes with gilt lettering.

It is *John Wesley's Journal* I must tell you
about. Not that there is much to tell, but
what there is goes to show, somehow, that God
helps those who help *others*. Harry says they are
an answer to prayer, and I wouldn't dispute
the matter with him for worlds.

'They came out of a hard winter,' said he,
having hedged me into his study—his retreat
from his wife and a family of two—for this
young and energetic local preacher declares
that he must have a wilderness to retire to if he
is to blossom as the rose.

Briefly, therefore, when the dark nights came,
every one at Harry's church, a church with
many old and feeble members, felt that diffi-
culties were multiplying. Once again they had
to face the old problem of Sunday evening
services in which older folk were unable to
share, Harry solving the problem by advocat-
ing 'convoys', declaring that black nights and
bad weather might help to guide young folk to

church, for the simple reason that they were piloting older ones. 'We'll be convoys,' exclaimed this young man with the bright, eager face. 'You see the idea, of course? All of us who think we're young will make a point of calling on elderly and nervous folk, and pilot them to service on Sunday evening, and to other meetings during the week!'

Easily said, it was not so easily done, for it took time; but Harry did *his* share, and most of the others did theirs, with surprising results. That, however, is by the way; for observe what happened to Harry, who had wanted a set of *John Wesley's Journal* for years, and had never been able to afford it, even though it is astonishingly cheap.

To begin with, William Truelove dare not venture to service unless Harry called for him, afterwards taking him home, which Harry always did when not preaching elsewhere. On the way they had to talk, of course, and Harry talked about the things nearest his heart—the Lord he delighted to serve, and the books he wanted to read.

Now William Truelove could not attend service one Sunday evening, so he asked Harry to call for Mrs. Fletcher, and Mrs. Fletcher, delighted with her escort, asked him to tea the following Tuesday. Harry did not really want to go, but he went to please the old lady, and

there he met her brother who had arrived unexpectedly. The brother said he liked two
pieces of sugar in his tea. He remarked that the
weather was mild for the time of the year, and
went on to say casually that a friend of his, a
widow, had asked him to find a home for *John
Wesley's Journal*, in eight handsome volumes
with gilt lettering, *and did Mr. Harry know anybody who wanted them?*

Harry did!

How fine they look in the study now, eclipsing
the linoleum, and giving grace and charm to
the room over the hall!

You see, therefore, how a shining Sunday
faith translated into weekday service really may
enable God to answer prayer, even in the worst
of bad times.

FANNY'S FATHER

IT WAS HARRY, if I remember rightly, who
told me about the Good Samaritan who, going
home one dark and stormy night, kicked something metallic. He bent down and groped on
the pavement till he came upon a bunch of
keys. Then he fought a battle with conscience.
Whoever had dropped the keys, he argued,
would want them as soon as possible. They

might even be locked out, and to be pacing the streets on such a night would be misery indeed. Should he pocket the keys for the time being, or turn back nearly a mile and hand them in at the nearest police station?

Conscience won. Back he tramped. He handed the keys in, and went into the night once more, bending to face the wind and rain, but glad in his heart that he had done the right thing.

For all that (and you should have seen Harry's face as he reached this point in a story he has worked into more than one sermon) life plays us scurvy tricks now and then, and this Good Samaritan felt his virtue slipping from him when he reached his own front door, put his hand in his pocket for his keys, and discovered nothing except the hole through which they had slipped.

I believe the moral Harry contrives to draw from this tragedy is that our patience is tried in order to make us still more patient, and that we encounter setbacks for the sole purpose of buttressing our souls. I have not the least doubt that Harry is right. In point of fact, I know that adversity is often the best soil in which to cultivate Christian virtues, and that sometimes we have to stumble through the darkness before we can find the light.

This thought brings me at once to the beginning of April, and a miracle.

His hat blew off. That was the beginning of my research into another man's faith.

It was a windy Sunday as I walked uphill. As chance would have it (if there be any such thing as chance in life), I happened to be close behind a tall fellow wearing a black overcoat, a black hat, and a black tie. He was carrying a bunch of daffodils. In another minute I should have overtaken him, for I was walking quickly, but a sudden gust of wind lifted his hat and sent it bowling merrily along the dry, white road. I made a dive for it, missed it the first time, but succeeded in taking it prisoner at the second attempt.

He smiled charmingly as he took it from me, thanking me as he did so. 'Ah,' said I, 'I see I have the honour of rescuing property for the aristocracy.'

'I'm afraid you are mistaken,' he replied, amused, I gathered, at my remark. 'But what makes you think so?'

'The aristocracy,' said I, 'never on any account run after their hats.'

Thus we fell into step, the only thing left for us to do, since we were going the same way; and thus began our conversation. 'A fine day,' I murmured, glancing furtively into his handsome face, drawn as if in pain. 'A day on which we ought to be happy.'

He nodded. 'I think I *am* happy,' he replied.

It was an odd thing to say. I was about to reply, but I held my peace, and presently he added: 'You'll have guessed where I'm going?'

'To the cemetery,' said I.

'Yes, to put daffodils on Fanny's grave. She died a month to-day, a little gift from God, lent for four springtimes only.'

'And her mother?'

'Died the day Fanny was born.'

We were walking less quickly now, for the hill was steeper, the wind against us, and our thoughts were upon this age-old problem of bereavement. My companion in black kept his eyes on the trees, green and feathery against a clean-swept sky, and on the thin spire rising above them.

'She was all sweetness and sunshine,' he said. 'There was never a merrier child; never one with such quaint ways. Heaven was about her from first to last. One day since Christmas she and I walked this way to her mother's grave, and on the way she came upon a twig, she picked it up, carried it to the foot of a tree, and said comfortingly, "Dere, little twig, your Daddy will tate tare of you." '

He was smiling as he spoke. 'And now,' said I, 'you have neither wife nor child?'

'That is so. But I'm proud.'

'Proud?'

'It has occurred to me during the last week or two, friend,' he replied slowly, 'that God must value me highly, otherwise he would not have treated me so. It seems to me that God must have some special use for me—if not, why shape me with so much care? I begin to see dimly, imperfectly, that for three years God was shaping me by means of my wife, and that for four years Fanny was shaping me, making me more sensitive to heavenly things, more responsive, less worldly, giving me the simplicity of childhood, the confidence of one who never doubted. . . .'

He was speaking so bravely and cheerfully that it was a shock to see the tears coursing down his cheeks. I waited.

'And now,' said he, 'I feel that sorrow has given me understanding, the ability to be sympathetic, the privilege of preaching a mighty faith—the mighty faith which Fanny never knew she had.'

We parted on the hilltop—he with his daffodils for Fanny, and I with a little prayer in my heart that this man, strengthened by what might so easily have made him weak, might ever preach the Resurrection Message by his life.

A LITTLE MAID AT SUNDOWN

MY CHANCE ACQUAINTANCE with Fanny's
father had something in common, I fancy, with
a few minutes I spent in company with a little
maid a week or two later.

It was evening, and so still that there in the
green lane, awash with gold as the sun went
down, I could hear no sound except singing
birds and the creak of a distant farm wagon.
I was alone.

At any rate, I had thought so—but then, as
Judith has been at pains to remind me on
various occasions, I often think one thing when
other people think another. Apparently I was
wrong in this instance, for as I sauntered in the
sunshine I became aware of a childish voice.

You know, of course, how unconsciously a
child sings, with no thought of creating an
impression, but only for the sheer joy of singing? So this child sang; and as I turned the
corner I came upon her as she sat on a green
bank, a heap of cowslips in her lap, her head
a little on one side. Unaware of my presence,
in a bright world all her own, she sat there
singing sweetly and softly.

She was not embarrassed when she saw me.
'Did you hear me?' she asked.

'Yes.'

'Did you like it?'

'Very much.'

'I'm glad. Do you like my cowslips?'

'Of course—and what a lot you've gathered!'

'Yes, haven't I? They are for the Sunday School Anniversary to-morrow.'

'Indeed?' I sat down by the little maid, a pretty picture in her blue frock, a blue ribbon to match in her rich brown hair. 'And are you going to take them with you?' I asked.

'Yes. You see, most of the boys and girls will take flowers from a shop, or eggs, or fruit, or things, only *we* can't afford any now that Daddy's gone to heaven. So Mummie said I could stay up late to-night, and gather lots of cowslips. I shall give them to Miss Smith, and she'll put them in a vase, and they'll stand near the pulpit. Afterwards, I shall take them to Mrs. Potter. She's been ill for years, only she never grumbles.' She sighed. 'I hope we have a good collection,' she added irrelevantly.

'I hope so, too,' I said. 'I'm sure you'll have a fine day.'

'Yes, I think so. I have a white frock, and I shall stand in the front row. I'm in the Primary. And I have a hymn to sing all by myself.'

'The one I heard you singing as I came up the lane?'

'Yes. Do you like it?'

'Very much, and you were singing it sweetly. Would you like to sing it to me now?'

'Yes, if you won't laugh. You'll pretend it's a *real* service, won't you?'

'I will.'

I lay back on the grass, closing my eyes, or nearly closing them, for I saw her put down her cowslips, straighten her frock, and look up at the sky as she sang her hymn.

She had, as I say, a sweet voice, and she sang accurately and unaffectedly, being lost in her singing. But that was not all her charm. It was something in the fervour with which she sang which made its appeal to me. I have listened to more than one famous singer, and I have heard many famous preachers, but I do not think I have ever been more deeply touched by singing or more stirred by a sermon than I was by this little maid as she lifted up her voice in that cathedral out of doors, the golden sunshine like a halo round her head:

> Walking every day more close
>   To our Elder Brother;
> Growing every day more true
>   Unto one another.

As she sang there in the stillness of the evening I felt that God was using her small voice to reach my heart. I did not speak for a moment or two after she had finished. Then I said, 'You love that hymn?'

'Yes,' she replied, gathering up her cowslips, '*and my Daddy loved it, too.*'

So we walked along the lane together, she with her cowslips, and I with my thoughts; and just before we parted near the village I slipped a piece of money into her hand. 'I'm sure you would like to put this into the collection to-morrow,' I said.

Then I hurried off; but, like Wordsworth, I could have said:

> The music in my heart I bore
> Long after it was heard no more.

HE ASKED WHAT HAPPENED

WHILE I AM RECALLING friendly adventures out of doors, let me tell you of a very different experience. In one sense, I suppose, it amounts to nothing, but I think perhaps you will forgive me for mentioning it.

One might imagine that all who walk in God's good world, especially in springtime, must surely come back refreshed in spirit. It seems, however, that this is not so. Anyhow, I know one man, at least, who somehow remains poor amid immeasurable riches. Let me tell you about him:

I was so busy that I left my desk and walked in the country.

It was late spring, and the day stands out in my memory in spite of the fact that I travelled only a little way and was away from home only a short time. Happily I live within easy reach of green fields and quiet woods, and in twenty minutes I was away from the houses, and in a world of wonder.

I will relate precisely what I did. I strode along the road till I came to the bridle path. There I slackened speed, wandering along till I came to the opening in the hedge where you may look far into the wood, with its dappled light and shade slanting across the shimmering bluebells. Hereabouts is the stump of a tree, and on the stump I sat down, lighting my pipe and remaining motionless for a little over half an hour. Then I went back along the bridle path, regained the high road, and so returned to my own door.

Before I reached home, and when, indeed, I was less than a hundred yards from the garden gate, Shearwater overtook me. I say *overtook* me, for Shearwater overtakes every one. 'How do?' he sang out. 'Been looking for that crock of gold again?'

This, by the way, is Shearwater's standing joke, for he has it firmly fixed in his head that my country walks are what he calls 'eyewash', and that whenever I set off I am really prospecting.

'I've been having a great time,' I told him frankly.

He grinned. 'Awfully exciting?' he asked, a trifle impudently, though he is an excellent fellow. 'Tell me just what happened.'

'Would you really like to know?' I asked, and when he fell into the trap, I told him. 'Shearwater,' I said ponderously, 'you've missed a treat. I've been along Easton Road. I kept on till I came to the bridle path—the white gate on the left which you may have caught sight of when dashing by in the car. Well, I was lucky this afternoon. I went along the path, as I say, turned a corner just where the path bears to the right round some hawthorn bushes, the hawthorn being in full blossom . . .'

'Yes, yes. But what *happened*?' Shearwater was always an impatient fellow.

'There was *more* hawthorn in blossom when I got round the corner,' I informed him. 'More than I've seen for years. So I went on under the trees, and through sunshine and shadow—just like life, you know, or like walking in a cathedral with the light streaming in through the windows and between the pillars. You'll know the spot where the hedge falls back, I expect?'

'Of course. What about it?'

'There's the stump of a tree. I sat down. I was very still, Shearwater. I didn't move for half an hour, at least, and *then*, what do you think?'

'Couldn't say. Go on, tell me what happened.'

I looked steadily at Shearwater, who has rather puffy bags under his eyes, and wears a somewhat expansive waistcoat. I smiled. '*Nothing*,' I said quietly.

'But you gave me to understand that something *did* happen,' he exploded.

'Well, in a sense it did,' I countered. 'You see, old chap, we live in a world where things are for ever happening, day and night, at home and abroad. Switch on your wireless and you hear what has been happening. Open your paper, and it is the same. Meet some one in town, and they shout the latest news at you. Don't you see, Shearwater, we are harassed and fussed and humbugged continually by *happenings*—and isn't it something of an achievement to have found, for once, a spot where *nothing* happened?

'You see,' I went on, 'I just sat there with the trees and flowers, with bluebells like the eyes of God, with the fragrance, and the stillness, the *stillness*, Shearwater, the stillness which was full of strength, and it was *because* nothing happened that it was all so wonderful. Do you understand?'

Dy

He said he did, but as he hurried off I wondered if he really did, and if he could.

Anyhow, I returned to my work like a giant refreshed, and I thanked God that He had kept for me a little corner of this crowded planet where nothing happens.

ST. MARGARET

I HAVE A NOTION that God has many such corners—places where it is easier to worship, somehow; people who help us to keep our faith. I think, for instance, of a woman whom I have long nicknamed St. Margaret. She and I invariably take tea on the last Tuesday in May, and we always sit in the small room on the right of the hall as you go in, a room with a window from which you may sometimes see anxious people going by.

The last time I called she began by reproving me. 'You really shouldn't, you know,' she murmured, as I pushed a small parcel into her hands.

'Madam,' said I, 'you are not trying to be cruel?'

'I hope not,' she said as I followed her indoors.

'Then,' said I, 'you must not rob me of one of my chief delights.'

Very sweet, very simple, very bright and cheery, and very understanding, is St. Margaret. 'And now,' I went on, 'please invite me to tea.'

So she did, and we sat there between a fire smouldering in the grate, and the mass of flowers on the table in the corner. We talked of many things while drinking tea and eating the small sandwiches St. Margaret had prepared. All the time, of course, we kept an eye on the window to make sure we did not miss any anxious people.

For St. Margaret is the patron of anxious folk. She was anxious herself once.

That, of course, was years ago, long before her hair turned white. I think she is only a little past fifty now, but it is difficult to tell, for she has a young face, radiant with a gentle sweetness, and white hair which makes you think she is older than she is.

She lives in a little brick house. She has a small garden. There is a maid who comes in the mornings and goes home in the late afternoon. Otherwise she is alone. But not many days pass before some one sits in the comfortable chair near the fireplace, and they always have a cup of tea.

It happens that St. Margaret's house faces a nursing-home. That is the point. That is its strategic significance. You might, of course,

imagine that such a position was a drawback,
but this is not so. For notice:

Into the nursing-home comes broken
humanity to be mended. It is not pleasant
having to go into a nursing-home. It is not a
joy facing an operation. Most of us know it.
But there is perhaps something harder. *It is
having to wait while a loved one goes through the
ordeal.*

You know what happens? The mother with
an only son, the young wife with her hopes
hanging by a thread, how are they to live
through those dreadful hours when their dear
one is in danger? The mother *cannot* stay at
home. The young wife dare not be alone. The
waiting-room is, at best, a chilly place, indifferent and rather grim. The woman who
waits is driven to pacing up and down the road
outside. She must spend, say, a couple of hours
which seem like a couple of centuries; so she
walks slowly up and down the road. She is one
of the anxious people upon whom St. Margaret
smiles.

She does it all so cleverly. By chance, as it
seems, she just *happens* to be going out at the
garden gate when the anxious person comes by;
or she is straightening her back after a little
imaginary weeding, and *chances* to look over the
low hedge. A bright smile, a kindly glance, a
word about the weather, and the contact has

been made. She listens patiently while the anxious person explains why she is there, for St. Margaret is too wise to appear to know; and then, as luck will have it, the lady with the white hair and friendly eyes says she *believes* the kettle will be boiling that very minute. She'll just run in to see. Would the anxious person care to take a cup of tea with her?

You see the deception of it all, of course? You see how the passer-by is enticed into the little sunny, friendly, comfortable, cheery room? St. Margaret makes tea, talks about her garden, the wonderful skill of doctors in these days, the hopes we may always cherish, the faith we can always cling to, and of that Great Physician who heals body, mind, and spirit. Thus the leaden hours are speeded, and a rare ministry performed.

I have reason to know how rare a ministry, for St. Margaret helped *me* through *my* dark valley. And I know why she goes on doing it year in and year out: It is because she once paced up and down that road, and the news she had at the end of her waiting was bad. So she asked God why—you see what a simple woman she is—and God said it was so that she might learn to help other people in time of need.

I have never forgotten what St. Margaret did for me. That is why I go to see her at least once a year.

As I look back over the year I see May giving place to June. I see naked trees clothed in living raiment, fields with waving corn like green seas over which shadows ripple after sunshine. I see the gardens growing lovelier every day; and I remember how glad my heart was when God made the earth fair again.

Winter changed to spring, and spring, you remember, blossomed into summer, with long days and kindly sunshine, the sound of singing birds, *and the hum of lawn-mowers*.

I mention the latter because I have the misfortune to have neighbours who are garden-lovers. I am a lover of gardens, too. I like to see trim lawns, and flower-beds aglow with colour. I could sit looking at them for hours on end. But I have not Mr. Middleton's zeal for mowing and weeding.

My neighbours, on the other hand, are energetic gardeners. They never fail to put me to shame every summer. That would not matter if it were not for Judith, who has very decided views on the duties of husbands, and must needs be my conscience, with the result that as surely as summer comes I am compelled to push the lawn-mower, or get down upon my knees and weed for dear life.

But even this punishment may sometimes be a blessing. It at least provides an excuse for looking over garden walls, and passing the time of day with a neighbour. I have more than once changed into my old clothes, put on my gardening shoes, searched for, and eventually found, a rake, and sallied forth to talk a couple of hours with a fellow gardener, discussing perennials in the friendliest way. Moreover, when wives are watchful and idleness impossible in one's own garden, there is always the possibility of an excursion next door for the purpose of admiring a prize lettuce, or borrowing a hoe.

REMINISCENCES

SUMMER, OF COURSE, brings other pleasures, among them missionary meetings and chapel anniversaries. Some of the happiest times I have known, I think, have been linked with country missionary meetings. Often I have been part of a bus-load of jovial Methodism (for Methodism *can* be merry on occasion), and have helped to support some country cause by sitting down to a farmhouse tea or supper, listening to a returned missionary from some lonely corner of the earth as he tells his story in some lonely corner of our land, and riding home in a twilight dim with rose. The world has seemed a friendly place at such times.

Once every year for I do not know how many years I have attended a Chapel Anniversary in the country, and I can say with truth that I have almost always come away with a song in my heart. Last year I came away with a bit of philosophy, too, and this was the manner of it:

There were two sittings-down after the service. My host and hostess (for as usual I was spending the week-end with two old friends) took it for granted that I should go with them to the Monday evening meeting, and I was glad to go.

What the church caretaker called 'two bus-loads o' folk' came in from other villages, and long before the service began the little chapel was so full that chairs had to be taken from the vestry. Miss Wilby excelled at the harmonium —so much so that when we came to the last verse of 'Great God of Wonders!' (sung to the rousing tune, 'Sovereignty', which, by the way, takes no little playing on a harmonium), one good brother called out, 'Hallelujah!'

But it was not the service I intended writing about. It was what happened between the first and second sitting-down at supper. The folk who had come from a distance were the first to sit down, and my host and hostess were so busy looking after them and supplying their needs that I was left to wander into the sunny lane, where I began chatting with our chairman, the prosperous Mr. James Wardlaw, who had come over from the neighbouring town. I understood he was a very successful building contractor.

There was something about Mr. Wardlaw which had impressed me from the first. I liked him. It had been his privilege, he had told us, to take the chair at the Chapel Anniversary for fifteen years. I happened to know that his subscription was more than all the rest of the collection put together.

'It's pleasant to come back to the old spot,' he told me as we walked slowly into the village. 'I was born here, you know. My old aunt lived in yon cottage at the corner—and I led her a dance, I doubt. There's been a few changes, and what is now the post office used to be Joe Pinder's cobbler shop.

'He was a character, was Joe, if ever there was one. He taught in the Sunday School, and kept white rabbits. A queer old chap, and no mistake. We used to plague him—some of us lads. His shop had a door with a brass knob, and many a time I tied it to a nail outside so that he couldn't open it. He never lost his temper, not even when we put a flat stone on his chimney and smoked him out of house and home.

'I remember one night three of us, Billy

Sparkes and Walter Hampson and I, broke into his yard when we knew he'd be at a prayer meeting. I was a wild lad then—an orphan, brought up by my aunt—and when I saw his two prize white rabbits, I said it was a shame that he should have *two* when I hadn't *one*; so I took one of them. I kept it in an old box in a shed at the bottom of my aunt's garden.

'I never quite knew *why* I did it, but I remember I was wretched about it an hour afterwards. I dare not take it back because Billy and Walter would have laughed at me.

'Three or four days later I was at the bottom of the garden when Joe came limping along. He was carrying a basket, and I remember I was really scared. I guessed he had come for his rabbit, and that Billy or Walter had let the secret out. He would accuse me of stealing, and though I hadn't thought of it as stealing at the time, I knew very well there was no other name for it.

'I shall never forget what happened then. He was a little old man with white hair, and a very deeply lined face. "Jim," he said quietly, "you've a white rabbit of mine." I could feel his eyes on me. All my cheekiness slipped away, and I couldn't say a word. As I say, it hadn't seemed like *stealing* till that minute, but it did then. "Well, Jim," he went on gently, "there's only this I wanted to say. I've loved you all along, nearly like a son, lad, and it grieves me to think you should *steal* what I would have been only too ready to *give*. I just want to tell you that I don't like to think of that rabbit being alone, so I've brought you its mate, Jim. *You can keep 'em both*." '

As we had come to the end of the street, we turned back, walking in silence. Then the chairman said, rather huskily, I thought, 'It takes a lot to make a high-spirited lad cry, but I burst into tears there and then; and there and then a new heaven opened about me. I'd never known that any one could *love* like that, and it made me understand something of the forgiving love of God. . . . I think I was born again in that hour.'

We returned to the schoolroom in time for the second sitting-down; and above all the rattle of cups and saucers I seemed to hear the refrain of that stirring hymn we had sung an hour before:

> Who is a pardoning God like Thee?
> Or who has grace so rich and free?

The chairman's story of Joe somehow brings me at once to Brother Webster, and what a few of us did for him.

It was really our third minister's idea, and that was perhaps why our worthy Circuit Steward, a most excellent man of business, but a stickler for precedent, was not altogether over anxious to see the plan executed.

Brother Webster knew nothing of the plot, of course. We speak of him as Brother Webster because, as far back as any of us can remember, he has called us all brother or sister. He was worshipping in the front pew of the east transept when I was a boy, and one of my earliest memories is of the laborious way in which he used to go down on his knees to pray, clasping his big hands together and bowing his head so reverently that what he did, and the manner of it, often impressed me more than the prayer I heard offered.

He was always at church, except when preaching in a village chapel—he never felt worthy to preach in the town pulpit. A good man he was, and you could *see* he loved the House of God.

One Sunday Brother Webster was not with us at church, and we learnt that he was not likely to leave his bed again. Somehow, the service felt queer without him, and it almost seemed unkind to sing when he could not hear us. I think the young minister had felt this, for it was he who persuaded some of us to go along one sunny Friday evening and hold a service outside Brother Webster's house.

Our worthy Circuit Steward, as I say, was not thrilled by the suggestion, but he consented to go with us. The choir supported us splendidly. In all, we mustered no less than sixty Methodists.

Brother Webster, propped with pillows, was in a bed by the open window. He lived in an almshouse facing a spacious green where children play, and he was able not only to see us but also to hear us. 'The idea', the third minister explained when he saw Brother Webster's astonishment, 'is that if *you* can't come to *us*, well, *we* can come to *you*.'

That was it exactly. There on the green, with the sunshine all about us, swallows skimming over the roofs, the fragrance of little gardens rising like incense to heaven, there, I say, we held our service, Brother Webster smiling faintly at the open window.

We began with 'All hail the power of Jesu's name', and though we had neither organ nor piano, we lifted up our voices in God's praise, singing all the louder because of the radiance which crept into Brother Webster's face. We sang even louder still as doors opened to right and left, as children gathered from the green, as working men and a few women came shyly forward, standing half-scornfully, half-wistfully, at the fringe of the crowd.

We prayed in the open air, a working man next to me instinctively removing his cap and taking his pipe from his mouth; and there was Brother Webster bowing his white head as of old, his big hands clasped till the knuckles shone. Then we sang the old hymn 'Come, Thou Fount of every blessing', to the tune 'Normandy', and because Brother Webster loved it so much we sang the last verse over again. There was a Bible reading, and an anthem by the choir; a short address by the third minister, and a closing hymn. No doubt our choice of the hymn seemed singularly inappropriate, but if you knew Brother Webster as some of us have known him you would realize that nothing could have been more appropriate than 'Jesus, tender Shepherd, hear me'.

How softly and reverently we sang the last verse in that still evening which God had given us:

> Let my sins be all forgiven;
>   Bless the friends I love so well;
> Take me, when I die, to heaven,
>   Happy there with Thee to dwell.

'And the grace of our Lord Jesus Christ, the love of God the Father, and the fellowship of the Holy Spirit be with us all, this night and evermore. . . .' It was Brother Webster who pronounced the benediction in a low, trembling voice.

As we went home something happened. Our worthy Circuit Steward (an excellent man of business, as I said) remarked in a curiously shaky voice: 'I don't know whether or not we've helped Brother Webster very much . . . *but I do know that trying to help him has helped me.*'

Besides the Chapel Anniversary and the open-air service for Brother Webster, June brings to mind two portraits, one of a young man, the other of an old one.

I recall sunshine, trees, good humour, and a deep serenity somewhere in England, and I remember how by chance I joined a group of spectators.

My original intention had been to push on to the next village, but the temptation to watch cricket played as it has always been meant to be played was too strong. My good resolution weakening, I strolled along the side of the hawthorn hedge till I came upon men and girls watching the home team at play.

HE STAYED AT HOME

THE HOME TEAM, all in white, was batting, seven wickets down and forty runs to make. Beyond the pitch, a green island, as it were, in a sea of golden buttercups, stood tall chestnuts and elms in the hall grounds; and to the right were the red roofs of the village, with here and there a peep of white walls gathered round the grey tower of the church, half hidden by a giant copper beech. A blue sky, sunshine, fragrance, a kindly breeze, a deep stillness broken only by the musket-fire of the bat as it struck the ball, and a low murmur among the spectators who occasionally gave a cheer or a little round of applause, all these I noted as I sat in the shade of a sycamore, cool as the shadow of a rock in a weary land.

As luck would have it, I happened to be next to the village gossip. He greeted me with a nod and smile. 'Just thought you'd watch a bit of *real* cricket, eh?' he asked.

'Yes,' said I. 'And it's all the better as there's no charge for admittance.'

He grinned. 'Aye,' he agreed frankly. 'It's the same wi' me—I never were one for paying if there's no need. But I'd pay sixpence to see this here match! Our boys is in fine form to-day, though it's hot; and they're putting up a stiff game. Joe Leng was bowled out a bit ago for fifty-three, but he asked for it. That's him on the left there, sitting by the girl in pink —as usual. Something may come of it one day. Well done, Westcott! Fine fellow, Westcott— made a century last week, easy.

'It's Austin that's facing the bowling. Keep an eye on him. Grand chap, he is. Lives next door to me—taken over his father's joinery business now the old man's sleeping in the churchyard. First class at cricket he is—the son, I mean, Maurice Austin; and he's what I calls a gentleman.

'He's a *man*, Austin is. Now look at *that*— neat, wasn't it? That's a boundary. When I say a *man*, I mean, you know, that somehow his religion don't make him soft, if you understand. It's church I stay away from, as you might say; but Austin is a local preacher, and very acceptable they tell me. I've heard him myself once or twice, and he's straight with it. You feel he *means* what he says. I reckon the churches and chapels would be full again if parsons had something they couldn't help saying, instead of saying what just sounds nice. Now, look at that, neat, wasn't it?

'Well, I don't make it all very plain—only I reckon if a man *lives* his religion it's worth having. Take what happened a fortnight ago last Thursday, for instance, and just keep one eye on Austin. . . .

'It was him that got up the outing to Liverpool. He worked for it for weeks, sold tickets, ordered the coaches—we had five of 'em—and nearly all the village went. A grand do it was, too, and lovely weather. We started off at six in the morning—and what do you think happened?

'Well, we was all ready for off, and some of the coaches had got going, when Austin just stepped out of the one I was in, and said, "Well,

Ey

have a good time, all of you, and be good".
Then he waved his hand, *and away we went
without him*.

'Now *that's* what I call a bit of something
fine. You see, every ticket had been sold when
an old body here, Mother Wilson we calls her,
said she'd like to go, because she hadn't seen
her husband's grave in Cheshire for near on
forty years. She has a son that's not quite all
there. He's getting on to middle age, but you
haven't to leave him for fear he has a fit; and
so, just at the last minute, Austin let her have
his ticket, you see, and he stayed behind—see
that, another boundary—to look after the poor
fellow.

'That's what I call playing the game—on the
field and off; and if Austin's religion can make
him do *that*, why, sometimes I just feel I'd like
a bit of it myself. . . . See that, neat, wasn't it?'

AN APOSTLE OF THE HIGHWAY

THE OTHER JUNE PICTURE begins at a turn
in the road.

It was there I saw him for the first time, his
jacket and waistcoat hanging on a gatepost
some yards away, his shirt neck open to show
the bronzed chest, his old hat a contrast to his

white hair, and his wrinkled and venerable face the picture of strength and peace.

He was swinging a scythe with the easy motion which comes only from long practice, a kind of Father Time upon whom I had come by chance.

He seemed glad of an excuse to rest, and when I stopped short in my walk and remarked that it was a hot afternoon, he leaned on his scythe, wiped the beads of perspiration from his forehead, and agreed with me. 'I'll just put an edge on the blade,' said he, 'and while I'm doing it—if you're not in a hurry—I'd like to tell you that you're talking with one of the happiest men in England.'

'I can believe it,' said I, as he smiled. 'I rather think life must have been kind to you.'

An odd smile played about his lips, and the fine eyes flashed. 'I'm turned eighty,' he said, apparently irrelevantly, 'and I've no regrets. I can look back over the years and say, as Job said of old, *Blessed be the name of the Lord.*'

'It is a great thing to be able to say,' I replied; adding: 'But Job only said it after first saying, "The Lord gave, and the Lord hath taken away".'

He looked up quickly. 'You know your Bible,' he said with renewed interest. 'Most of them don't.'

'Most of them?'

The eyes twinkled, and the hand which held the whetstone was still. 'The folk who come this way,' he said; 'hikers, bikers, young men and girls in shorts, anybody and *everybody*. That's why I asked for this job. They mostly stop and have a word.'

'And I'm one of your victims, eh?'

He chuckled. 'Aye, if you care to put it that way. There was no need for you to speak, you know, but they mostly do. Well, now, you think I've had an easy life? That's the way of it, isn't it? But it has *not* been easy. It's been hard. My own mother left me to die on a door-step, and I had to take care of myself from being a little one. I worked and saved and scraped to get married on twenty-five shillings a week, and when I was well on the way to sixty I had my chance, and I took it.

'I began a poultry farm on a biggish scale, my four sons, all grown up, helping to run it. The war took them, every one. All four were killed in France, and it broke their mother's heart. I went bankrupt—I just couldn't work the farm in the circumstances—but I paid twenty shillings in the pound within five years. I'd a roof over my head then, but later a road-widening scheme came along, and the house I'd helped to build with my own hands was pulled down, and I was left with nothing to do, and nowhere to live. That was twelve years ago, and it was *then* I became a roadman.

'But this is the point: In prosperity I thanked God at our weekly prayer meeting, and when misfortune came I saw that God had chosen me to show my neighbours and friends that a man *can* believe in God in adversity as well as in prosperity. I've never missed that class meeting, and I've never ceased to believe with all my heart that behind the dim unknown standeth God within the shadow, keeping watch above His own. . . .

'And this bit of work on the road helps me to preach to all who'll stay and listen—same as *you* have done. This road's my pulpit; and my text is that a hard and apparently disappointing life hasn't made me bitter, and hasn't robbed me of my faith.'

When I left him he was hard at work again, swinging his scythe, a green lane of peace behind him.

AN OUTING

WHILE I AM IN THE COUNTRY let me tell you about four ladies I came upon quite unexpectedly.

There happened to be a notice outside the cottage. It said TEAS, so I went in.

As there was a large blue and silver car drawn up outside the creaking wooden gate, I told myself I should find company indoors. I was right, but I confess I had not imagined that I should come upon quite such a group of oddities. I had thought that perhaps some well-to-do gentleman and his wife might be sipping tea in the cottage, or even that I might have to nod to a dashing young fellow and his fiancé, but I found very different people in the low-raftered parlour where the sunshine seemed at home, and the red brick floor and small tables with brown china had a warm and friendly look.

Near the window was a dapper little man whose smiles ran up from his cheeks to his high forehead, and ended in a shining halo where his hair should have been. For company he had four shabby women, all of them the worse for wear.

The lady of the cottage mothered me into having tea and hot buttered toast, and while she went to fetch these delicacies I had time to note my companions. One of the four ladies wore a black coat and skirt, a black hat, and a pair of black gloves with which she fanned herself rather ostentatiously. I gathered that she never went anywhere very important unless it happened to be a funeral. One of the women had very hard hands, and a very long, wrinkled

face, and a very wide hat which had certainly
seen better days, and I heard her say that it
would take her half the night to tell George all
about it. There was a very plump woman in a
faded purple costume much too small for her.
She had brown gloves, and an umbrella; and
there was a little shrivelled woman who seemed
hard of hearing, and was all the time leaning
forward and saying, 'Speak up, can't you?'

Not that they needed the injunction, for all
spoke loudly. ' "Go on," I says,' observed the
woman with very hard hands, ' "wot d'ye
want me at two o'clock for?" I says. "And on
Saturday, an' all?" But there it is, you see,
when you think your 'ouse is fallin' down, a bit
of good luck comes your way, don't it?'

There was a general chorus of assent,
especially from the little shrivelled woman,
though I doubt if she had heard a word. The
dapper gentleman murmured something which
I did not catch, but I saw the smiles coursing
up his pleasant face, and the sunshine from the
window behind him made a brighter halo
than ever.

Presently there was a commotion when they
took their departure. The dapper man piloted
the funereal-looking woman down the garden
path, and I noticed that she limped badly. He
returned solicitously for the others, and I could
not help smiling as I saw the shrivelled woman

glance round furtively and then snatch a tiny
piece of white lilac, stuffing it inside her coat.
Presently the four women were in the car, but
the one in purple came hurrying back, picked
up the umbrella she had forgotten, pushed a
penny under a plate, and then, with a nod to
me, said triumphantly, 'Good hafternoon,
mister. We're four ladies hout for a houting!'
With that she bounced out again.

'A quaint party,' said I to the lady of the
cottage when the big car had vanished.

She smiled. 'Everyone thinks that,' she said,
'when they see Mr. Henry on Saturday afternoons. He's rich, but his wife's been an invalid
for years. They called here every Saturday
when they were courting—my mother had the
cottage then—and when she became bed-
ridden, Mrs. Henry, I mean, she made her
husband promise to bring a party of poor
women here every week. I know her quite
well, and sometimes spend a day with them.
She's ever so sweet, and she says this is *her*
afternoon *off*—thinking what a happy time
charwomen and the wives of the unemployed
are having *for her*, as she puts it. The Unemploy-
ment Exchange help to find the people,
Mr. Henry runs them round, and the lady at
home in bed asks God to bless them all.'

THE SINGING CONSPIRATORS

THIS MENTION OF AN INVALID brings to mind one of the happiest incidents of my friendly year. I told Judith about it as soon as I returned home, and when I said that the young lady in question was exceedingly pretty, my wife made a gallant attempt to regard me suspiciously. She failed, however, to look jealous (having had little practice) and her frown quickly gave place to a mischievous smile. Nor could she blame me for chatting a moment or two with the invalid, for one of Judith's weaknesses is collecting old and infirm ladies to whom she furtively conveys tea and honey and fruit drops, and the like, thus wasting my substance in riotous giving.

As I say, she was exceedingly pretty.

I came upon her at the foot of the hill, a corner with a cottage in a garden filled with summer flowers and shaded by fine trees. Close by was a stone wall overflowing with cataracts of valerian.

I should not have stopped to speak had she not been in a bath-chair. She was young and full of life, it seemed; and she was Tony's sister.

I had never heard of Tony, but it was not

long before she was telling me about him, and
about the conspirators; for after a few pleas-
antries, during which I leaned against the
stone wall, she chatted away as if she had known
me all her life.

'It was so unexpected,' said she. 'Yes, Tony
is a member of the rambling club, and loves it.
He walks twenty miles and thinks nothing of
it.'

'And you?' I asked.

She smiled, a little wistfully. 'Oh,' she
replied, 'I can *think*, and that's nearly as good,
you know.'

'You do not walk, then?'

'No. It's spinal trouble. It began three or
four years ago. It was terribly hard at first—I
loved tennis so much, and swimming, too.'
She sighed, but she looked up brightly to say,
'Only, life's still thrilling, and it gets more
so'.

'I'm glad,' said I, daring to look again at the
face which was not just pretty, but had something like serenity in it. Then, to change the
subject, I added: 'I suppose you live in this
lovely spot? You don't happen to be the good
fairy in the cottage across the way?'

She laughed. 'Oh, no,' she said. 'I live ten
miles off.'

'Ten miles?'

'Or more!'

'Then how do you come to be so far from home?'

So she told me of the conspiracy. 'It was Tony, really,' she explained. 'You see, he *loves* walking. Well, a week or two ago he became very mysterious. One day he carried me downstairs—I'm not *very* heavy, you see—and what should I find but a new bath-chair? The old one had solid tyres, but this one has pneumatic tyres, and is specially upholstered to suit a peculiar person like me.

'Well, one day he began being deceitful.'

'I am sorry,' I murmured.

'Yes,' she laughed, 'it's sad, isn't it? He and the others put their heads together, and they plotted a plot. Before ten this morning the rambling club was singing one of my favourite songs outside our house, and then Tony picked me up, and put me in my chair, and the rest of the singing conspirators began fighting for the fun of pushing me.

'Up hill and down we've come, singing nearly all the way. We had lunch at a village inn an hour ago, and now they've negotiated this steep hill—though how we'll ever get up again, I don't know. The rest—listen, they're coming back—have gone to see the ruins. I *made* them.' (There was a touch of sweet imperiousness about the way she said it.) 'I wanted to be alone and quiet a minute or two—

so that I could thank God for all His goodness.

'Listen—there they are. There are twenty of them, and we're having tea at a farm miles off, and they're going to *push* me all the way. This is one of the loveliest days of my life!'

I moved off as the conspirators came into view. 'Come on Ton-and-a-Half,' cried one freckled young man with bare knees. 'It's *my* turn to do the donkey-work. Now then, all you miserable sinners, I'll bet you can't sing going uphill!'

But couldn't they? I stopped to listen; and presently I turned to look. Up went the bath-chair with Tony's sister in it; and the last I heard of the conspirators was their young voices as they sang:

> When we walk with the Lord
> In the light of His word,
> What a glory He sheds on our way!

THE ROUNDISH MAN

ALTOGETHER UNEXPECTED was my meeting with the girl in the bath-chair, and unexpected, too, was my momentary acquaintance with a heroic gentleman who refused to allow adverse circumstances to conquer his spirit. I refer to the man with whom Judith and I rode a mile or two when we invested a shilling in a mystery drive.

'There's nothing either good or ill, but thinking makes it so,' murmured the little man. 'That's Shakespeare, madam. Or we might say there's nothing *outside*—everything's *inside* us, as the professor remarked after a seven-course dinner, referring, of course, to the mind. It doesn't matter what happens *to* us, madam; but what does matter is how we interpret it. I'm afraid I don't make myself plain—but can I help being good-looking?

'To illustrate the point, take the case of the romantic young lady who was staying at a sweet little cottage in the country. One morning she went down to breakfast exclaiming, "Oh, Mrs. Higgins, while dressing I listened enraptured to the gurgling of the little stream at the bottom of the garden. . . ."'

' "Nay, miss," said Mrs. Higgins, "I doubt you was mistaken. That there noise was just father having his porridge." '

'Now, madam, what I wish to point out . . .'

The roundish little man broke off abruptly as the coach came to a standstill with a sudden grinding of brakes. It was sagging badly at the off-side, and a prim lady next to us was visibly alarmed.

'This,' remarked the roundish gentleman, beaming upon her, and the rest of us, 'is the *mystery* itself. We were promised a surprise, and here it is, a burst tyre. It is a very fortunate thing.'

'Fortunate?' The prim lady's eyebrows went up.

'Precisely, madam. I believe *one* tyre has burst. Now, where should we have been if *all four* had burst? Which reminds me of a ministerial friend of mine who sat on an air-cushion and burst it, whereupon the dear old soul he was visiting began sobbing. "Now you've done it," she wailed. "That's the very end of my poor, dear departed husband. He blew that cushion up almost with his last breath, *and now I've nothing of him left at all.*"'

I ought perhaps to say that Judith and I were on holiday, and that for fun we had invested in a mystery drive. The coach (if one might call it that), due to leave at three, had been twenty minutes late in starting. There were two lovers in the rear, a man and wife who never said a word from beginning to end, three ladies who did nothing but complain of the jolting, the prim lady, the roundish man, and Judith and myself. We should have looked like a funeral party if it hadn't been for the roundish man, who told funny stories all the time, was gallant to the prim lady, and kept informing us that he *must* get back by five, as he had a very special appointment.

The life and soul of the party, the roundish man beamed upon us all as if we were his family. He glanced smilingly at the back of the coach where the young lady would certainly have fallen out, had not the young man put his arm round her; and I believe he winked at the prim lady.

'You see,' he went on, 'a tyre has burst. It is a warning that we do not any of us get too puffed up. Suppose we complain—we only make matters worse. If we make the best of it, it's better. Let us, then, improve the shining hour by observing that we book our seat in a coach, go for a run round, or a *jolt* round, as you might say, and end where we began, or *hope* to do so. We end, I say, *where* we began, but not *as* we began. The Israelites in the wilderness ended pretty much where *they* began—*but not as* they began.

'Life, of course, is a circle. We begin in darkness and we end in darkness, but during the journey, my sweet friends, ah, during the journey, we change, we grow, we are refined, so that the soul awakes and spreads its wings.

'What? The spare wheel's on already? The man's a marvel! I'll hand my hat round on his behalf—and if I'm lucky, I'll keep that appointment for five o'clock prompt.'

He did. We were back where we had started at five minutes to five, and as we got out of the coach he remarked, 'And now for it! I've been racked with toothache all the afternoon, and five is zero hour at the dentist's. However, there's nothing either good or bad, but thinking makes it so. Good-bye!'

It has been my privilege in the past to spend a part of August by the sea, where I have almost always met some friendly soul in the crowd. During the year I am bringing to mind I came face to face with a retired bank-manager and a ragamuffin.

In point of fact, the retired bank-manager was my host, a very worthy Methodist called James. A greater contrast than the one between the dignified James, respected resident of a fashionable watering-place, and the ragamuffin it would be hard to find. It is seemly, therefore, that I speak of James first.

A charmingly courteous man, my host is blessed with the saving grace of humour. I have heard him say more than once that not even sixty years of Methodism have knocked all the fun out of him.

My hostess complains that James is the worst husband she has ever had.

Very pleasant they have always been, these two, and very pleasant they were the last time I stayed with them. It is hardly surprising, therefore, that not till Sunday morning did I begin to notice that things were different. At a quarter to ten I was waiting for my host among the roses in the spacious garden, but he did not appear, a most unusual thing, seeing that he has been sidesman as long as I can remember, somehow combining that important office with the office of society steward. Formerly he and I had always walked to service in time to arrive before ten. On this occasion the three of us (my host and hostess and I) did not leave the house till ten minutes past ten.

We sat in the family pew at the back of the church, James at the end so that he could easily step into the aisle in order to take up the collection. But when the collection was announced James did not stir.

After service I expected to walk home with my hostess, leaving James to count the collection in the vestry; but, to my surprise, Alice went up with the minister's wife, and my host and I took the promenade way home.

'Then you are not society steward now?' I asked.

He shook his head, smiling whimsically. 'Not now,' said he.

'Nor sidesman?'

'No. They have a younger man instead, as you would see. It seemed a good idea to have some one really good-looking, by way of a change.'

'You still write the pulpit notices, though?'

FY

'No. We have found a man with a type-writer, and the result is that even our visiting "specials" can read the notices now.' I knew he was laughing at me as he spoke.

'And the afternoon Sunday school?'

'I've given that up for a time.'

'So you don't hold any office in the church, now?'

'I'm still a trustee, of course.'

His answers were brief. I glanced at him furtively to see if there were anything hard or grim, but the lines about his mouth were as kindly as ever, and it seemed to me that he knew not how his face shone. I had detected no bitterness in his tone. 'But you have been so active all along,' I said. 'I used to think the church here would never get along without you.'

He nodded gravely. 'Yes,' he agreed, rather surprisingly, 'I used to think that, too!'

It was an illuminating confession. I waited for him to explain.

Smilingly he said: 'I haven't taken offence since you were here last. I'm not at cross-purposes with the Super. I don't think I'm growing lazy, and I've only resigned for the time being. I dare say I'll be society steward again, if I live—and if Alice will let me—but at the moment I go to church to *worship*. Only don't let that astonish you!'

The lips were still humorous, but he became more serious as he went on: 'In the first place, I resigned because I was keeping younger men out of office. That was something. In the second place—and this was the real reason—I was aware, deep in my soul, that I was coming to church much as I used to go to the bank, because I had to show people in, or count the collection; because I held office; because it was expected of me. . . .

'Things came to a head one wet Sunday evening last October when a "local" was planned. "Alice," I said, "if I thought there would be some one else to count the collection, I'd stay in this evening."

'Do you know what she said? She said, "James, if that's how you feel, you *must* stay in this evening".

'I saw it then. I saw that church-going was becoming mechanical, that I was eaten up with a sense of my own importance. I realized that the oftener I went to church in that spirit the farther I was travelling from the Kingdom.

'So, for a time I'm letting the soil of the spirit lie fallow, hoping God's rain and sunshine will revive it; and this evening I'll go to service, not to show people to their seats, but to ask God to come into my heart. Do you understand?'

I said I thought I did.

A CASTLE BY THE SEA

To come, so to speak, from the sublime to the ridiculous, allow me to introduce a rough little customer who drew my attention to himself by remarking: 'I bet you're too old to dig!'

It was a challenge, and I responded instantly. Picking up a wooden spade lying close at hand, I began making the sand fly in first-class style. Under the pitiless sun (it struck full upon the back of my neck) I toiled like one of the Israelites of old, nor did I weary in well-doing till the two rascals and I had raised one of the tallest, proudest, and most symmetrical castles on the shore.

It was hard work beating the sides till they were smoothly rounded, the heap rising like a cone above the deep trench into which Charlie poured water. I said unto him, 'Fill another bucket from the pond,' and he filled it; and I said, 'Do it a second time,' and he did it a second time. And I said, 'Do it a third time,' and he said, 'Oh, blow! Let's put Adrian's flag on it.'

So we did, and bravely it fluttered in the battle and the breeze, all the boys and girls thereabouts looking at it with envy, which pleased the three of us very much, all of which goes to show we are far from the Kingdom.

Then we threw ourselves down—we three fine fellows, Charlie and Donald and I. We were hot with our hard work, and tired, too; so I strode across the crowded shore, and demanded three cornets from an ice-cream vendor; and when I had paid for them I returned unto the waiting two, who greeted me with loud cheers, the possibility of my buying three cornets for myself never having entered their heads.

Picture us, therefore, lolling behind our sand-castle—of which we were still inordinately proud—and licking ice-cream cornets, for the best people *lick* cornets, and only the riff-raff close their lips over them.

You must know that I had never before set eyes on these rascals. Only by chance had I appropriated a square yard of sand close to their pitch, and there I had immediately knocked up an acquaintance with Charlie and Donald, discovering that they were among a party of twenty-five city urchins who had been brought to the seaside for one day only. The other twenty-three, it appeared, had gone, at their own expense, for a sail in the *Sea Witch*. 'But we're saving *our* money,' Charlie had told me. Before I had been able to ask why, Donald had butted in with the mad challenge, 'I bet you're too old to dig!'

Lying there in the sun (cooking in a slow oven, it seemed), I said: 'And who's Adrian?'

'My big brother,' replied Charlie, who was seven.

'Yes,' said Donald. 'He's twelve, he is.'

'Quite an old man,' I murmured. 'How long has he been shaving?'

'It's him we're saving our money for,' Donald informed me ungrammatically.

'Indeed?'

'Yes. We've got sixpence each to spend, and we're spending threepence each, and buying Adrian some rock with what's left. It will have the name right through.'

'And why hasn't Adrian come on this trip?'

'Oh, he couldn't. You see, father's only just got work this week, the first time for two years, so he *had* to go; and mother's very poorly with washing floors, and her back; and there's Betty (she's five, and can't ever be left because she is a bit funny, and doesn't always know what she's doing), so Adrian just *had* to stay behind, you see. He wanted to come, and he *would* have done if father had been off work; and he was looking forward to coming, but he pretended he didn't mind. He gave us a flag that somebody had given him for being good; and he asked us to put it on a sand-castle for him.

So we have done—and, goodness, you didn't half help, didn't you?'

Before me rose a vision of a little hero of a down-town neighbourhood; and as I parted with a piece of silver I asked Donald and Charlie to tell Adrian it was from a friend who had seen his flag flying, and had saluted it.

WILLIAM THE GRUMBLER

FROM THE SEASHORE we will go inland, if you please, leaving the cool breezes and coming to a spot where the August sun is fiercely hot. Here it was, as I well remember, that a voice growled: 'If only them lasses 'd 'urry with them custards it'd be a godsend, I'm thinking.'

I agreed with William, and so did Percy and Joe, who were on the wagon.

William, turned seventy, is as brown as a berry. He and I were labouring in the harvest field, each with a pitchfork, each tossing up sheaves of wheat to the crew on the wagon.

It was a blistering afternoon. The field, ochre-coloured, was on the sunny side of the hill, the heat intense. As we moved from one stook to the next I would look with shaded eyes at the golden land stretching away into a blue haze, to the trees beyond the field, and over the gleaming stooks on which the pitiless sun glinted as if striking burnished metal.

A privileged novice, I was making myself delightfully stiff. Dressed in old trousers and an open shirt, I toiled hour after hour, taking care, however, not to get a pain across the shoulders, or to make the skin peel off the palm of my right hand.

'Them there young scallywags,' muttered William, referring to George and Robert, the farmer's sons, 'ought to hev been looking after these here hosses, they did, instead of chasing rabbits.'

To have heard him you would have concluded that he was the most disgruntled of all sinners—had not the smile which lit up his venerable face belied his voice. 'Shoving nettles into my pouch, an' all,' he went on reminiscently. 'Break every bone in their body, I will,' he added.

From his lofty position on the wagon, Percy suddenly called out the welcome news that he could see 'summat white a-comin'!' We cheered.

'It'll be custard,' said Joe excitedly. 'I saw Betty putting six of 'em in the oven.'

'Bin longing for a bit of custard for the last couple of hours, off and on, dang me, if I haven't,' muttered William.

We all fell to discussing the custards, for which Wold Farm is famous, wonderful kitchen triumphs over four inches deep, the crust firm and light, the custard, like a bath of gold, deliciously cool and sweet and refreshing to men labouring in the hot sun.

We had just reached the hedge, with its welcome shade, and were flinging ourselves down in the jungle below when the two girls came up. They brought us home-brewed ale, and two great custards, each cut into four quarters. The sight of them made glad our hearts.

As I think of that picture, round about four in the hot afternoon, I see Percy and Joe lying on their backs; and I see Sally and Margaret standing, arms akimbo, as they declare laughingly that all four of us are not worth the exertion of crossing *three* fields. I see William grumbling about the extraordinary small size of the huge custards, his face full of rare sweetness as he speaks. And then I see two ragamuffins coming down like wolves on the fold—George and Robert, sweating, panting, whooping, as they break through the hedge and cry, 'Custard! Excelsior!'

'The very thing!' shouted George with boyish enthusiasm.

'Saved our lives!' Robert declared, winking at Sally.

And then there fell a silence, one of those little lulls in conversation which last only a fraction of a second, but *seem* to last an age. Probably every one saw the difficulty at the same moment. With the two boys there were *six* of us for *eight* quarters of custard. The silence was broken by William who was muttering in that odd way of his: 'Well, you chaps can eat custard if you want to. A pipe's all I want, really, though I could do with a bite first. I reckon if us four hard-working chaps has a quarter of custard apiece, there'll be a half each for these two dratted scallywags.'

Five minutes later he was tossing up sheaves again, and I thought I heard him humming to himself.

Am I growing foolish? Is it absurd to see in this little harvest-field incident some faint shadow of Sir Philip Sidney's shining deed with a cup of cold water on the field of Zutphen? William, no doubt, would growl out something to the effect that I was suffering from a touch of the sun.

EMPTY PEWS

AFTER HARVEST and harvest-thanksgiving the work of the new connexional year rushes into the autumn and winter programme before some of us know where we are. The sunburn is scarcely fading when we are once again attending week-day meetings, the busy round of church life again in full swing.

Sometimes our hearts are in it, and sometimes they are not, for it is not always easy to bring the irresistible energy of springtime into our autumn campaign. In latter years there has been much to disappoint and dishearten those of us who are jealous for the effective witness of our Church, and September is the month in which we need a spiritual tonic and a challenging vision more than at any other time.

At any rate, this is how it seems to me, and for this reason, if for no other, I think it wise to recall a September week-day when a new flame was kindled in my heart.

There had been a service in the afternoon.

'But of course,' one of the society stewards had murmured, 'no one expects a crowd in the afternoon. It isn't reasonable.'

About three hundred folk had been catered for by the ladies responsible for the five o'clock tea. Eighty people were present, including the ladies themselves.

An air of disappointment pervaded the large schoolroom. The unused cups and saucers, row upon row of them, reminded one of lost souls, somehow.

'I remember,' the society steward murmured, 'when we had to borrow crockery from the

Prims—and I've seen the lecture-room packed with people, a kind of over-flow tea-room.'

At the great evening rally, held in the chapel, the Circuit Minister estimated the congregation at a hundred and fifty. The society steward, having taken a peep through what he always called the minister's door, returned gloomily to the vestry, cheering the visiting preacher by saying bluntly: 'There's only a handful of folk scattered about the body of the chapel. I've known the day when we had chairs in the aisles. . . .'

'It's not a very favourable evening,' murmured the chairman, toying with his programme.

'Things are rather bad just now,' the Circuit Minister pointed out.

'Collections will be down,' grumbled the society steward.

'Isn't it time to begin?' asked the visiting preacher.

It was; so in they went—into the great church built by men of faith, and left by them as a silent challenge. A half-hearted service it was. The singing had no volume. The chairman's remarks, though witty, did not really create a happier or more helpful feeling. The caretaker, more depressed, it seemed, than the society steward, saw no reason for switching on the lights over the gallery.

At last came the familiar phrase: 'I have great pleasure,' said the chairman, still toying with his programme, 'in asking our young friend to give us his message.'

Then stood up a young man with radiant face and burning eyes. 'Mr. Chairman,' said he, and his personality was electric, 'you have been regretting that there are so many empty pews. I am not sure I agree.

'I remember, sir, once coming upon a boy who was reading *Robinson Crusoe*, and when I saw how thrilled he was, I wished I had never read the book so that I might have the delight of coming to it freshly and wonderingly. I am not sure, sir, whether I would rather have these pews full or empty. They may be filled too easily, sir, filled with men and women who wear their religion lightly.

'Empty pews are a direct challenge. They give one the joy of trying to fill them, the thrill of doing something big, of proclaiming the gospel with all one's mind and heart and soul, and of doing even more than that, *of living it out every minute of every day*.

'Why are these pews empty? Because the world is indifferent? Because of these sad days? Because I am not a conjurer? Sir, we ourselves constitute the reason. God has not changed. Jesus still saves! The gospel is glorious and powerful as ever. *But those who advertise it have lost their vital force,* their first sweetness, their blazing passion, their shining dreams, their inextinguishable enthusiasm, their inexpressible joy, that madness of theirs which is the only real sanity in the world. . . .

'Let us turn this occasion into a service of witness! Let us own that we've betrayed our Lord. Let us admit that we cannot give Jesus to others *because we've lost Him ourselves.* . . . And then let's find Him again here and now, gloriously, in reality, by prayer and faith. Come, Holy Ghost, our hearts inspire!

'*Dear God, make us Thy hands and feet and tongue, and let us never tire till there is not one empty pew!*'

'Amen,' murmured the society steward, his face aglow.

THE OLD, OLD STORY

BUT THERE IS NO NEED to go indoors to worship, no need of formality, *if only the heart be on fire*. The evening service in a wilderness of empty pews had something in common, I fancy, with an odd adventure I enjoyed soon after. It happened one gusty October day, and it amounted to so little, and yet it seemed to me to count so highly that you may think nothing of it, or much.

There had been rain, but towards evening the sun broke through ragged clouds, and I walked in a golden world afire with God.

Up the hill I went, the very lane aflame, the earth so filled with shining wonder that I needs must sing.

Or try to, for I am not blessed with a voice which is a joy to others, though it pleases me quite well.

Thus it came about that I sang:

> Tell me the old, old story
> Of unseen things above,
> Of Jesus and His glory,
> Of Jesus and His love!

Striding along the lane with its burnished grass and rich foliage drenched in blazing light, I sang to my heart's content. It was something of a shock, however, after singing the second verse, to hear someone I could not see taking up the refrain:

> Tell me the old, old story,
> Tell me the old, old story,
> Tell me the old, old story
> Of Jesus and His love.

Breaking through the vivid light of the western sun, the voice was strong and resonant, a magnificent tenor which put me to shame and silenced me (as I thought) for ever.

He came into view at last, a man of middle-age. Dressed in rough clothes, he had a bundle of sticks under his arm and a dog at heel. 'And the best of it is,' he declared as he advanced with long strides, 'it's true!'

'I'd no idea any one was within earshot,' I assured him, 'or I'd have remained silent!'

'And why?'

'I've a profound regard for the well-being of my fellow men.'

'Then let's finish the hymn! Perhaps some other pilgrim on life's rough road will hear us, and get to know the same Jesus that has filled *our* hearts with joy. Come now: Tell me the story softly . . .'

It was ludicrous for me to join in with him, for his fine voice drowned mine, and his tenor soared up far beyond my rumbling bass. But we sang, for all that.

'It's an old, old song,' said my singing companion, 'and there's many folk would laugh at it. It's not up to date, I admit, and perhaps it isn't great poetry. But it's about the one thing that makes life worth living to-day! Jesus and His love . . . it's all so silly and worthless unless you really know what it *means*. It's like being in love, one can't help thinking the whole business a bit stupid till you suddenly find yourself up to the neck in it, and *then* it's the the only real thing in life, the biggest driving force in the world, the sure defence against the slings and arrows of outrageous fortune. Yes, He's come into *my* life in a blaze of splendour, just like this flaming sunset. He's flooded my soul with light and life. Let's sing again with God's sunshine on our faces, and God's fresh air in our lungs, and God's good spirit in our hearts. Come now, join in, and we'll have the loud pedal for the refrain!'

He was irresistible, this amazing farmer who talked like a boy. So we sang the hymn again, making the echoes ring with the refrain; and as we sang I forgot to laugh at myself, ridiculous though I must have seemed. I forgot I'd never meant to go beyond the highest point of the lane. I forgot everything except the ecstasy and rapture of that golden moment when the sun went down in a swirl of fire, and the two of us stood facing it as we lifted up our voices and sang:

> Yes, and when that world's glory
>   Shall dawn upon my soul,
> Tell me the old, old story—
>   Christ Jesus makes thee whole!

'And now,' said my farmer friend, 'to come from the mountain-top of exalted experience to very ordinary but necessary affairs, you'll have supper with me? The wife will be glad to meet a chap that has something to sing about.'

Gy

I protested, of course; but I went.

If you knew (as Judith knows to her sorrow) how badly I sing you would be surprised that I have dared to record the fact that I ever lift up my voice. Nevertheless, I delight to hear others sing, if only they sing better than I do, which is almost always the case. You will not, therefore, be surprised if I find room for this little story of what happened in an hotel in which I was staying last October.

Coffee, I remember, was served in the lounge. We could hear the rain beating on the windows, and every now and then a gust of wind shook the building. The Colonel, one of the most cheerful of all the guests, remarked that winter seemed to have returned; and then, having lighted a cigar, he forthwith sank into his chair, sighing deeply.

There would be thirty or forty of us. The Misses Collins were not there—two R.A.F. men having taken them to a dance. Neither were the Wintertons and Lesters, both families having gone to the theatre, in spite of the advice they had received to the contrary.

I will not say the guests were out of humour, but several who had intended going out were staying in against their will, and as there were far more ladies than gentlemen, even whist and bridge appeared to be falling flat. By ten the guests had arranged themselves into little groups. Some were still whiling away the time with cards, others chatting. Several were reading, and three—the Colonel among them —were asleep.

'Can't any one recite "Mary had a little lamb"?' Miss Parker demanded loudly and plaintively, a kind of half-hearted challenge in her tone.

'Or bring a white rabbit out of a hat?' piped Mr. Waterlow, a tubby little man with pink cheeks.

'One would think you were in the Cabinet,' murmured Miss Parker, giving Mr. Waterlow an arch smile, 'making an inane remark like that.'

There was a little laugh, and a few guests pushed a card-table aside. 'I suppose no one can sing?' someone threw out.

'Miss Joan, here, sings,' declared an eager young gentleman with sleek black hair. He smiled encouragingly as he spoke.

Miss Joan, the girl in blue, shook her head. 'Oh, no, really,' she said. She was not pretty, but there was charm about her, and her simple frock, dark hair, and fresh complexion signalled her out among the guests. Indeed, there was something very sweet and natural about her. One would hardly have classed her with quite a number of the guests, and yet it would have been hard to say where the difference was to be found.

'Just *one* song,' pleaded the Colonel, now wide awake, and gallant as usual.

In vain she protested. Her first objection was that she had no music, but the sleek young gentleman said in a loud whisper that she could sing and play without it. He *knew* because the other afternoon he had been surprised . . .

We applauded encouragingly, and Miss Joan obliged.

And how she sang! Hers was a voice in a thousand; rich and clear, sweet and full, perfectly controlled, magnificently used. Song after song she sang, accompanying herself. She thrilled every one, and whenever a song was finished the Colonel rose and bowed, murmuring his thanks. An old Scotch air, 'Bless this House' ('even though it *is* an hotel,' she added laughingly), and 'There'll Always Be an England', these were among the songs she sang.

Then, when she had threatened to sing only one more, and had sung many, she said: 'Let's all sing together now.'

Her fingers swept the keys. She gave us a chord, and we joined in with Keble's immortal hymn, 'Sun of my soul'.

Never shall I forget it. The hotel lounge became a church. The very card-tables were altars. The bored guests—and this was the wonder of it—knew every line of every verse.

You should have seen the sleek young man singing. You should have heard Miss Parker singing. You should have caught sight of Mr. Waterlow, the tears trickling down his pouchy cheeks; and above all our voices rose one clear voice like an angel's, for the girl in blue was carrying us all out of this shadowed present into a shining eternity:

> Come near and bless us when we wake,
> Ere through the world our way we take,
> Till in the ocean of Thy love
> We lose ourselves in heaven above.

When the hymn was done the Colonel remained silent.

MRS. PARKER'S NEIGHBOUR

WITHOUT BETRAYING any confidences I may say that the Colonel hinted on more than one occasion that he had seen a good bit of life, and had travelled in every continent. I was, I trust, duly impressed; but I venture to think that however wide the Colonel's experience he is unlikely to have explored much of Mrs. Parker's world.

I made her acquaintance by accident one

November evening, As the bus was crowded I gave her my seat.

She was a large, shapeless woman, with greying hair under a jumble-sale hat. She held a brown-paper parcel, and her hands were red and coarse. She did not sit down. She sagged. 'Eh,' she said, 'I'm nearly beat.'

She looked it. 'You'll be glad of a cup of tea,' said I, availing myself of the curious privacy one always enjoys in a crowded bus.

'You're right,' she agreed. 'First thing I'll do when I get home is make myself a cup of tea, and a strong one. If I don't, I'll collapse—and then where should we be?'

I didn't know, so I made no reply; a piece of discretion which some of our diplomats might emulate.

'We'd all be done for, I'm thinking,' she declared, sighing again. 'Things has come to something nowadays, and no mistake. With my husband in bed these four years, and our Annie's two kiddies living with me, I don't know how we're going to get through, I just don't.'

'Oh, you'll manage *somehow*,' I said. 'I'm sure of that.'

She looked up. 'That's nice of you,' she told me, becoming confidential. 'And funny, too.'

'Funny?'

'Why yes, you saying that there to me, I mean. *You* won't think so, but it is, because them's the very words I keep on saying to Mrs. Parker. She lives next door, poor soul.'

'Your neighbour's in trouble, I gather?'

'Well—aren't we all, these days? Only, you see, she isn't used to it, same as I am, in a manner of speaking. I was born poor, and I've been poor all the time, and scrubbing other people's floors has been my job mostly, because Henry was never much good, at best. But Mrs. Parker, well, *she* lived in a semi-detached once, and she's come down in the world. I said to her week afore last when I was doing her bit of washing for her—she's dazed just now with her husband being killed in the railway siding —I says, "Mrs. Parker, you'll manage somehow," I says, just as you did now. That's what made it seem funny, you know.'

'I see.'

'And I said it again every night last week, me sleeping at her house, so to speak. She's that down, I'm afraid of her doing away with herself. So I goes in about eleven, and I just mends a few things for her two little ones. I had to sit up half the night with the poor dear Monday and Tuesday of last week, but she's coming a bit better, I reckon. She says God's forgotten her, and I says to her, " You'll manage somehow, even if you haven't no husband," I says. "God'll take care of you, same as He has of me, all along—though it's never been easy." Only, it's no good me giving her medicine and not taking it myself, so I'll just cheer up a bit—and I'll be all right after a cup of tea.'

'Let's see,' I murmured, 'what's her address?'

'Mrs. Sophie Parker, seventeen Blackburn Row, and I live next door—fifteen. I always tell her she's two up on me! And this is where I get out, I'm thinking, and thank you kindly. . . . I'll tell her she'll manage somehow.'

I raised my hat.

Darkness had gathered, but there was light and music in my heart. Thanking God for one of His everyday saints, I hurried along to a grocer friend of mine, and between us we arranged to send a little load of surprise to number fifteen Blackburn Row. On the flour bag I wrote: 'God doesn't forget. *You'll manage somehow.*'

HE CAME BACK

MRS. PARKER'S NEIGHBOURHOOD was no better than the one in which lived a little hero whom I always think of as 'the boy who came back'.

It would be the last Saturday in October, or the first in November, when I called between three and four in the afternoon. I knocked at the front door, but got no reply; so I went round to the back door of the gaunt house—you know what a weakness I have for back doors—and surprised a boy shaking a hearthrug.

He flushed when he saw me. 'Hallo?' said I. 'You didn't hear any one knocking, did you? I thought not—that's why I came round to see if there was any one at home. Your mother—is she out?'

'Yes.'

'I see. She's usually in on Saturday afternoons, though, isn't she? Do you know when she's likely to be home?'

'About five.'

I pondered a moment or two, taking the opportunity it afforded me to glance again at this boy with shirt-sleeves rolled up, hair tousled, face grimy. He was still flushed. As it happened, I knew something of the household. I knew that the father had died a few months before, and that he had left a widow and two boys, Peter, aged eleven, Donald, a weakly laddie of six. I knew also that there was precious little money to keep a roof over their heads, and that Peter's mother had had to begin charring.

'Where's Donald?' I asked.

The boy with the rug in his hands hesitated. 'Mum sent him to Mrs. Shipman's,' he said, awkwardly. 'He's staying there for the afternoon. She's had to go out. Some people are moving in to-day, and she promised at the last minute to scrub down for them. She didn't want to go on a Saturday afternoon.'

'I see.'

Somehow we didn't seem to be getting anywhere. The boy was, so to speak, on the defensive. I had caught him unawares, almost as if I had surprised him in the execution of some crime. I noted the bucket and scrubbing-brush in the scullery, and also the coarse apron the lad was wearing. 'I rather thought you would be at the pictures,' I remarked casually.

He coloured again. 'Mum thinks I am,' he declared, almost defiantly.

'Indeed?'

'Yes. You see, she only made up her mind to oblige these people early this morning, and she had the baking to see to, because she was out all day yesterday. So she sent Donald to Mrs. Shipman's, and she gave me threepence to go to the pictures.' A new light came into his eyes. He had suddenly decided to enlist me in the conspiracy, it seemed. 'She locked the house up when she went off after dinner,' he told me, 'but I didn't go to the pictures. *I came back.*'

'And climbed in through a bedroom window?'

He stared. 'You didn't see me, did you?'

I smiled. 'No,' I admitted, 'but I did things like that when I was a boy.'

That loosened his tongue. His eagerness carried him away. 'You see,' he confessed, 'I'm sorry for Mum. She's working day and night, and when she comes home about five this afternoon she'll expect she has to begin cleaning up here, scrubbing the floors, and doing the grate, and washing the windows, and shaking the mats, and brushing the stair-carpet, and all that. And so,' a trace of the flush returned, 'I just thought I wouldn't go to the pictures this afternoon. I came back, and crept through the back bedroom window, and I've got a lot of the cleaning up done, and she'll just be ever so surprised when she comes in— and I'll have tea ready for her, and I'll fetch Donald home, and she'll just feel, you know, she'll just feel, you know, that somebody *loves* her, won't she?'

I looked down at the boyish face, and I felt there and then that God is not without His junior saints. I was deeply stirred, but I think my voice was matter-of-fact when I spoke, for I said casually, 'I say, old chap, you wouldn't do me a favour, I suppose? I was thinking of going to the pictures this evening, but I haven't a pal. *You* couldn't come along if I looked round about seven?'

He managed it.

I thought it awfully good of him.

JOAN

My happy relationship with the chivalrous young gentleman who was not afraid of house-work tempts me to introduce another of my young friends, a very little maid for whom I have a great respect.

I ought perhaps to say that when I close the door of my study (Judith insisting on giving it that impressive name, though I invariably refer to it as the workshop) the world knows (or ought to know) that I am not to be disturbed. Sometimes I close my door because I really *am* going to work; and sometimes I close it because I am only pretending to work—just as the best Methodist parsons do from time to time. However this may be, it is to be distinctly understood that my study is my sanctuary, my fortress, my refuge from the prying world— which, in spite of anything Judith may say to the contrary, is wholly indifferent, for the most part, as to whether my door is closed or open.

Well, as I was saying, I was visited one November morning by a very little maid. It would be as well, perhaps, if I explain that now and then I like to think I am of some consequence. Very rarely some one taps discreetly at my door and apologizes for intruding, and when that happens I am ready to give them the half of all I possess, for I really feel then that I am being rightly assessed, though modesty forbids me to say so.

On the day of which I write (smiling reminiscently as I do so) I was sitting at my desk in the privacy of my study when the door opened unheralded by any discreet preliminary tap, and Joan entered without so much as an apology.

'Come with me,' she said imperiously.

It occurred to me that I ought to tell her I was writing, and that it behoved me to be majestically alone in order that no one might see me referring to a dictionary when doubtful about the spelling of five-letter words; but it also occurred to me that Joan, with the frank, brown eyes, the mass of curly hair, the yellow frock, and the tiny parcel wrapped in newspaper, might not appreciate all this vast significance, and the thought made me humble.

'They have a high handle,' she informed me. 'I can't reach it, and nobody comes when I knock.'

That was a hint, anyhow, and I made a mental note to have the handle of my study door raised another six inches. 'Whose door?' I asked.

'The lady in bed.'

Very probably you, being frightfully dense, would have failed to connect a door-handle and a lady in bed, but as I am a very astute (and also a modest) fellow, I understood Joan to refer to Mrs. Hargreaves, who had been ill for some weeks. 'You have been across the road to Mrs. Hargreaves?' I asked, 'and you can't get in. Is that it?'

'Yes. I knocked, but nobody heard me. So I knocked again, but they didn't again. So I've comed here. Please will you open it for me, and please hurry or it will be cold.'

'You've been baking?'

Her eyes lit up at once with pride and pleasure. 'Yes,' she said, putting her parcel on my desk and opening it. 'Look! Mummie is busy making cakes, and so I made a little pasty, and it has real jam in it, and the jam comed out of the big jar in the cupboard. I put it in the oven, and Mum said I could take it to Mrs. Hargreaves, and I wented, only nobody heard me, so I've come to you.'

'That's very nice of you, Joan,' said I. 'I'm frightfully busy at the moment. . . .' (Notice how stuffy we grown-ups are!) 'But I *think* I could spare a minute or two. And what a lovely little pasty you've made!'

'Yes, isn't it? I did it all by myself. I would have made one for you, but there wasn't time, and you aren't poorly. Come on, let's go. I like doing things for people.'

I resented this undue haste, for I am one who loves a peaceful life, but the very little lady dragged me out of my sanctum (I must have PRIVATE printed on the door, I think), down the stairs, and across the road to Mrs. Hargreaves', where I knocked softly. We were admitted by the housemaid.

Eventually I escorted Joan to the bedroom where Mrs. Hargreaves was slowly fighting her way back to health. 'Please,' said Joan, rather timidly, 'I've bringed you this little pasty. I made it all myself, and I put some jam in, and my love as well, and it is warm now. Would you like to eat it?'

'Very much indeed,' said Mrs. Hargreaves. 'I'm *sure* it will help to make me well and strong. It looks delicious—much better than the doctor's medicine.'

She began nibbling at the pasty, a smiling woman with a pinched face as she lay in the morning sunshine. 'Do you know,' she whispered a minute later, 'I'm feeling better already. It's wonderful . . . wonderful!'

Joan looked at her with rapt attention.

Then, in an awed whisper, she said, 'It was gentle Jesus told me to come'. There was a queer silence in the room, and for a moment I could have thought there were four of us instead of only three.

When I went back to my study I felt more important than ever before—realizing that I had been privileged to help a very little lady to do the Master's will!

A BEAUTIFUL LADY

HAVING SOMEHOW BROUGHT you to my study it seems natural to take a step into the educational world, which is precisely what I did one November afternoon when I understood afresh the important service we may render in obscure places, and how greatly we may enrich mankind, even though we are not well off.

Come with me, then, to a classroom a few minutes before the boys and girls put their books away.

In my mind's eye I can see her now as she beckons me. She turns from the blackboard, a piece of white chalk in her hand, adjusts her eye-glasses, and says quietly, 'I'm so glad you've come. I shall not be more than a minute or two.'

'Don't let me interrupt,' I murmured. 'Please go on.'

'I'm just giving some of the boys and girls their homework,' she explained. 'You must excuse my hands—chalk makes such a mess of them. I never feel clean in school. Yes, Sheila, you may clean the board; and Roy, you might see that the pens and rulers are put away when the class dismisses.'

I stood by her desk, looking on while this grey-haired teacher in a little country school brought the day's work to a close. Even then the afternoon was growing dark, snow-clouds gathering once more as the winter day hastened to its end. Books were closed. Bags were brought out. The slow boy of the class hurried up. Silence and order prevailed, and presently hands were placed together, heads bowed, and eyes closed as prayer was said in a low and reverent tone. The next moment there was a kind of war-cry outside—school was over for the day.

We stood talking, the schoolmistress and I, the boy putting away the pens, and a girl changing the water in a small vase. The teacher placed a sheet of blotting-paper in an exercise book.

'You'll be marking these this evening?' I asked.

She nodded.

Hy

'So the day isn't over for you?'

'Not yet.'

'Aren't you tired?'

'Well, perhaps a little.'

'You love the work?'

'I could not go on otherwise.'

'You would be paid.'

She did not reply at once. Instead, she gathered up more books, put the register in a drawer, nodded a 'Good night' to the boy, thanked the girl, and then remarked, 'I count for more than all the dictators.'

It was a strange speech for a modest woman, a bombastic assertion for a teacher in a little village school. I glanced through the window at the lonely valley, white in the snow, the trees black against the dark clouds, and I wondered what exactly this woman meant, though I think I had some idea.

'The dictators,' said she very quietly, 'shape from the outside, regimentation, I suppose. I spend my life shaping these boys and girls from the inside. It has been as much a consecrated task with me as that of being a missionary. I have drilled them, taught them, helped them, loved them. In my hands they have been as clay to the potter. I helped to shape their parents. I am shaping the children now, or trying to.' She sighed. 'Trying to give them the power to think, and to think for themselves. So far as I can I am teaching them what life holds in store, what they can make of it. Every night before I go to bed, I pray for each one by name.'

'And every day you make an altar of your teacher's desk?'

'Something like that.' She looked up, smiling suddenly. 'It gets very dusty,' she remarked.

'It seems to me,' said I, 'that you spend your life sowing seed. Do you ever gather a harvest?'

'Every day, in one sense,' she replied. 'Very rarely, in another.' She paused. She had lifted up the exercise books, as if to lead the way to her room. 'Only last week,' said she, 'a minister took prayers for me. He is young and full of idealism, a powerful preacher, a man of God. Once'—I thought her voice quivered slightly— 'he sat in that desk at the back, near the window. He used to come to school with his pockets full of caterpillars. When he was here the other day he said it was something I had said in class which made him turn to God. . . .'

She took off her eye-glasses, and there, in the fading light, I thought that this country school-teacher was indeed a beautiful lady.

UNDER THE STARS

WELL, THAT WAS AT the beginning of
December, and December, however churlish,
is the friendliest of all the months. It must
ever be so, for as long as there is Christmas
there will be kindness for a season.

If a man were to lose faith in his fellows for
eleven-twelfths of the year, he might still get
it back again as Christmas approaches, for of
all times this is the best—a kind, forgiving time,
as Charles Dickens reminds us, and a time when
nearly every one forgets to *grab* and learns to *give*.

Thrilling beyond measure is Christmas. I
love it for its carols, its holly and mistletoe, its
secret preparations, and its little plots and
counterplots, all designed, not to hurt, but to
make glad those we love. I like to see the shop
windows ablaze with light. I like to come upon
children gazing through the plate-glass into
fairyland. I like to meet mothers and fathers
hurrying home with brown-paper parcels. I
like to see young lovers standing at a jeweller's
counter and enjoying the delicious excitement
of choosing a gift which in after years will
recall for them one of the most precious
moments in all their lives. I like to answer the
door and be wished a merry Christmas. I

like to have heaps of letters and cards. I like
the smell of apple-sauce. I like the parties
which follow the festive season. In a word, I
like the generous, kindly, good-humoured
spirit which Christmas conjures up; and I thank
God that it is like a wedge driven deep into our
hearts—God's way, perhaps, of preventing
them closing altogether.

I bring this friendly year to a close with a
memorable adventure under the wide and
starry sky. I remember how unpleasant the
day was, cold and damp, and as unlike Christmas as any day in December could be. It was
difficult to believe that only two days separated
us from the most thrilling morning in all the
year. It had been cold when Judith and I had
gone down to the station. It had become
colder as the train roared through the twilight;
and long before we reached Heston Parva we
were both almost perished, though neither
would admit it—Judith having no regard
whatever for the truth.

At the best of times there is precious little
of Heston Parva to see, and at the worst (arriv-
ing by train) there is nothing but two faintly
yellow lamps half-heartedly illuminating a few
yards of the station platform, a kind of stage
whereon the station master makes his several
entrances and exits, much as Shakespeare's
melancholy Jaques, afterwards being heard no

more till another traveller presents his ticket and vanishes into the night.

It was barely six when Judith and I arrived, but darkness and fog enveloped us. There was a suspicion of frost, and a sneaking little wind which sent a fine drizzle into our faces, making us so damp and cold and wretched that we wondered what on earth had possessed us to leave the warmth and security of our own home. Happily we had only to cross the line to hear a voice saying, 'Here you are! Good. This way. . . .'

A shadow loomed out of the night that covered us. 'Get us into civilization in double-quick time, Arthur,' I pleaded. 'Judith's too cold for words.'

'First time I've ever known a woman as cold as that,' murmured Arthur, throwing our suitcases into the car, and then swinging out of the station yard and up the hill. We drove up the road, past the vicarage, beyond Thompson's Farm (I know every one there and love them all), over the bridge, and by the Twelve Apostles (tall elms I could only just make out against the darkness), and so to the old house where Arthur writes books and his wife cooks excellent dinners.

'I hope there's a fire half-way up the chimney, old man,' said I. 'I hope there's a fire big enough to roast an ox. I tell you, once my slippers are on my feet—if my feet haven't fallen off—I'll toast them on the hearth till midnight, and not all the king's horses and all the king's men . . .'

There was no need to finish the quotation, we were there!

It was after seven by the library clock when two travellers, warm, comfortable within, and thankful for the good things of life, were exchanging news and views as quickly and intimately as friends alone know how. Judith and our hostess were, as one might say, in heaven on the settee; and I had just drawn an armchair up to the blazing fire and begun filling my pipe from Arthur's tobacco-jar when he remarked: 'I want you to get thoroughly warmed, old man.'

I glanced up at my host, tall, humorous, greatly beloved. 'Thanks,' I said guardedly. 'You've expressed that wish three times already this evening.'

'Can a host be too solicitous for the welfare of his guest?'

'Well, no. But I'm suspicious by nature.' I paused. Then I added: 'I say, Arthur, you're not suggesting that I am to turn out again a night like this, are you?'

'Precisely that,' he replied, nodding affably and relieving me of the tobacco-jar. 'In less than half an hour.'

'But, my dear fellow, this is criminal. I'll be found dead by the roadside in the pale light of morning—starved to death, your guest! My dear Arthur . . .'

'Nevertheless, we're going out.'

'Tell you what,' said I suddenly, stealing a furtive glance at Judith, 'take *her* with you. She's awfully good company. I'll stay in and look after your wife. It would never do to leave two unguarded women in the house alone.'

To my consternation the two women joined forces with Arthur. 'The fact is,' said he genially, 'we're joining the carol-singers at half-past eight. That's partly why I wanted you to come over a day earlier this Christmas. You've been here summer and winter, but you've *never* been here just about Christmas-time. I'm going to show you—if it isn't too dark—what there is to see.'

Arguing with Arthur is always waste of breath, but I cannot say I was thrilled at the prospect, and I would have given anything in reason to have been left alone by that fire. However, Arthur had made up our minds, so off we went.

A more wretched night you cannot imagine. It would have been freezing had there been no mist. Not a star was to be seen. You opened the door and looked into a wall of blackness. A colder night, dry and star-lit, would have been infinitely preferable. 'Well,' said I, stamping my feet on the path as we set out, 'this is a *nice* way to treat your guest, turning the poor fellow out as if he were a criminal.'

'And guiding him,' said Arthur, shining his torch on the path, 'as if he were a lost soul.'

'We shall probably *both* be lost,' I muttered. 'We'll walk into a pool, or over a precipice, or something. . . .'

Cautiously we picked our way across the field-path, a short cut, Arthur explained, to Windrush Farm; and presently, my eyes becoming accustomed to the blackness, I could make out the hedge on my left, and see a fence two yards before we came to it. Soon the clammy wind bore the familiar strains of the Christmas hymn, 'While shepherds watched their flocks by night', Arthur remarking (in a voice which seemed full of darkness): 'They've started. Come on, we're late!'

I was in no hurry to rush to my doom, but I followed Arthur. Slipping now and then where a streak of ice lingered after the thaw, I crossed a fold-yard with mud squelching underfoot, caught the warm smell of hay and manure, and walked headlong into a party of the merriest people I have ever met.

I could see them as they moved in the yellow beam from the kitchen window of a farm-house, catching the glint of metal as the lamplight

fell on musical instruments—bugles and trom-
bones. I saw round red cheeks puffed out under
hats and above thick mufflers; and I saw, too,
that there were young men and girls. Some
were singing lustily. There were nine country-
men with musical instruments, and fifteen
singers—eight men and seven girls—most of
them young, though Harry Dodds, who sang
tenor, was turned sixty, and Joe Winthorpe,
who led off every time, was over seventy.

We joined the company at once, and as we
hadn't instruments of torture (as Peter Barlow
whispered to me when he ought to have been
playing 'O come, all ye faithful') we sang as
heartily as we could.

We were standing on damp ground. We had
fog round us. We felt the fine rain soaking into
our coats and hats, and driving into our faces,
for the wind was rising and becoming colder
all the time, but we heeded these things not at
all. There was something thrilling about singing there in the window-light (and by the light
of our own lanterns dimly burning); and we
were singing the most glorious songs in all the
world, the songs about the coming of the
Saviour of Men, God's priceless Christmas
gift to mankind.

We had no time to freeze, no time to grumble,
barely time to beat our hands together and
stamp our feet before singing another Christmas

hymn. When the repertoire was completed, Mrs. Major Potter appeared at the door, inviting us into the kitchen. How we all got in was a miracle, but then miracles *do* happen even in these days. We partook of ginger wine and mincepies; and we all talked at once, which was a good thing because it kept us warm. Then we wished Mrs. Major Potter a merry Christmas and a happy New Year, she and her two boys and her three daughters, and every one else under her roof, and Arthur sought me out (as we were getting ourselves through the door, not to mention the instruments and lanterns) and whispered that Mrs. Potter had done well to run the farm ever since her husband had died five years before, and that she was making it pay, too.

Again we plunged into the night, and the singers went before, the players on instruments following after, though there were no damsels with timbrels, and the young men took care of the girls, and the old men winked because they'd done it themselves long before; and the lanterns made little swinging patches of light down the muddy lane, and Arthur explained that the carol-singers went night after night, making about forty pounds for chapel expenses, and that they visited the Hall, White Barn, a score of farmsteads, and other places, being well received everywhere.

All this was broken into by Jimmy Miles, who assured me that one winter it was so cold that when they reached the top of Berry Brow they were all frozen in ten feet of snow, and that they played 'Christians, awake', for thirty-six hours without stopping; and he then asked me to believe that Bob Dyson, who played the flute, once paid his own railway fare to Aberdeen (three hundred miles each way) to play just one note in a band contest. 'And would you believe it,' asked Jimmy Miles, 'would you believe it, he was so anxious to get that note blown in the proper place, *he went and missed it!*'

We took our stand outside Swallownest Farm and played and sang with all the zest of good Christians. Far over the hills and far down the winding valley our music and voices floated. We sang 'The First Nowell' because it was Farmer Maddison's favourite carol, and then we went indoors and drank more ginger-wine and ate more mincepies, all in duty bound; and some of us tried our best to escape the mistletoe artfully placed over the door by Mr. Maddison's two unmarried daughters, and some of us didn't.

Still we went on. We turned up the wettest, muddiest lane in England's green and pleasant land, singing our loudest for Dick Marfleet, a queer old chap who lives alone. He came to the door to thank us, holding a candle over his

head, the flame flickering back against the
draught, his wrinkled face lit up with a
heavenly smile. 'God bless ye, God bless ye,'
he whispered, quite overcome, I thought, that
we should have gone out of our way for his
sake. It was all we got there—not a penny-
piece, but it was a *benediction* we would not have
been without.

Then we went over the hill, where the ice
crackled now and then, and down to another
farm where Mr. Chatterton and his wife had
hot coffee awaiting us, besides big fires in the
kitchen, the back kitchen, and the parlour; and
as if this were not enough, they pushed a handful of hot chestnuts into our hands as we filed
out again. What fun it was eating those chestnuts in the dark and cold, Arthur thoughtfully
shelling some for Sidney Warcup, who had as
much as he could do to carry his bassoon,
without trying to open chestnuts.

'You know,' said Sidney after a word in
praise of Arthur, whom he styled a real toff,
'you know, you might think us fellows was
doing this here for other folks. Don't you
believe it. We does it to put Christmas in our
own hearts, you see. It wouldn't be Christmas
for *us* if we didn't make it for somebody else.'

Still on! The drizzle had cleared, but the
wind was still rising, and a bitterly cold wind
it was as it struck from the snow-covered hills.

Three more houses we visited, among them a cottage by the main road, the home of two old folk who had only the pension to live on; and then we made for Eli Horsfall's farm.

It was uphill all the way. We left the high road. We left the lane. We took a track across the fields again, laughing as we missed our foothold now and then, singing softly to warm our lungs, opening gates and closing them, plodding across the stackyard, scaring the geese, and then rapping thunderously upon the front door. After cheering mightily we called out, 'Blessings upon thee and thine, Mr. Horsfall'.

The door was opened, and in we went. We were shown into a huge parlour. In one corner was a four-poster bed, and in the bed a white-haired angel. She was Eli Horsfall's wife, and she lay there like a queen, propped with pillows, a shawl about her shoulders. I was one of the last to enter the room, and observing that the outer door was open (the one leading to the stackyard) I turned to close it, but Jimmy Miles laid a hand on my arm and restrained me. I wondered why.

The family had gathered in the room. Eli himself told us he was right glad to see us once again; and his wife, her eyes dancing, her thin hands clasped, said she had been looking forward to our coming for a whole year.

We played and sang.

I don't know if you have ever heard a brass band in a parlour, but if not, you have missed a treat, providing only the players know how to modulate their tones. Our musicians played, and we sang, 'While shepherds watched their flocks by night', followed by 'O come, all ye faithful', and then, 'Hark, the herald angels sing!' After that, to give the singers a rest, the band played 'Deep Harmony,' and the woman in the bed lay with a rapt face. Then we all joined in one or two Christmas hymns, finishing with 'It came upon the midnight clear'.

As the last notes died away, singers and players alike bowed their heads, as if, indeed, a secret signal had been given. There was complete silence in the room, the old-fashioned room with its soft lamplight and its white-haired woman. I closed my eyes, and though I could not see who was speaking I knew it could only be Eli's wife. Her voice was wonderfully sweet. She was praying:

Lord Jesus, dear Lord Jesus, the fields are dark, the night is cold, the hour is late. Blessed Lord, there's light and warmth within this house, and the door is open wide. Come in, Lord Jesus, come. Abide with us for ever. Rest here and be at home. Little Jesus, come.

We all said softly, 'Amen'.

Half an hour later we were going our several

ways under a clear sky, for the wind had swept the clouds away. 'It was a wonderful prayer, Arthur,' I said softly as we hurried back by way of the high road.

'Yes,' he agreed. 'And a wonderful lady who prayed. She has been lying there nearly thirty years. She fell from a pair of steps when an angry stable boy kicked them; and she's borne no resentment all the time. She's a saint of God—you can see it in her face.' And then: 'I wanted her to make Christmas in *your* heart, old man. Was it worth leaving the fire?'

A church clock a mile away was striking twelve. The fog had lifted, as I say, and the stars were shining in the Christmas sky. 'I'm glad I came,' was all I said, thankful that he could not see my face.

*Printed in Great Britain by The Camelot Press Limited
London and Southampton*

SUMMER: '*I see naked trees clothed in living raiment.*'